Book 3

Sciencewise

Discovering Scientific Process through Problem Solving

Series Titles:

written by
Dennis Holley

illustrated by
Ellisa C. Holder

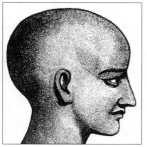

© 1999
CRITICAL THINKING BOOKS & SOFTWARE
www.criticalthinking.com
P.O. Box 448 • Pacific Grove • CA 93950-0448
Phone 800-458-4849 • FAX 831-393-3277
ISBN 0-89455-679-7
Printed in the United States of America

Table of Contents

Creative Challenges

This book is dedicated to
my wife, for her patience and understanding;
my parents, for encouraging me to wonder and explore;
my students, for teaching me more than they will ever know.

Introduction

The most beautiful thing we can experience is the mysterious. It is the source of all true art and science.

—Albert Einstein

There seem to be two aspects to the uniquely human enterprise we call science. One aspect is the continual search for natural truths. The other aspect is the vast matrix of facts and knowledge. Unfortunately, many parents and students, most textbook publishers, and even some teachers have the mistaken notion that science is memorizing terms, names, and facts. Nothing could be further from the truth.

Science is built up with facts, as a house is with stones. But a collection of facts is no more a science than a heap of stones is a house.

—Jules Henri Poincare

Science cannot be gleaned from the glossy pages of a pricey textbook. Science must be experienced, not memorized. Facts and knowledge are really the accumulated fruits of centuries of scientific labor. Make no mistake, humans are able to use these facts and this knowledge in the most incredible and creative ways imaginable, but facts alone are not science.

Imagination is more important than knowledge.

—Albert Einstein

The true essence of science is the relentless and unwavering need to know "why." It is this need, this nagging, irresistible curiosity to search for answers, that drives our species from the depths of the ocean to the blackness of outer space. This is what science really is,

and kids of any gender, color, and practically any age, with the proper guidance, can <u>do</u> real science.

Unfortunately, not only do students come to you not fully understanding science, they also lack the skills necessary to <u>do</u> science. They do, however, come through your classroom door fully charged with the most important precursor to scientific inquiry—curiosity. With this remarkable inquisitiveness, students, with your help, can begin to learn the skills necessary to <u>do</u> science. There are five basic science skills students need to develop: observing, predicting, designing/experimenting, eliminating, and drawing conclusions.

Observing

Science done right requires students to be accurate and thorough observers. Learning good observation techniques requires much practice. Hand in hand with the development of these skills must come the realization that any observation is the unique perspective of the observer, colored and altered by his/her experiences, expectations, and emotions. Students must constantly be challenged to separate inference (what they think is there) from reality (what is actually there) in their observations.

In the field of observation, chance favors the prepared mind.

—Louis Pasteur

Predicting

Curiosity raises questions. Careful observation reveals information. Using this information, we make predictions about the possible answers to our questions.

Prediction is probably the easiest skill for students to master. The main problem you will encounter is that students are often reluctant to make predictions for fear of being wrong. This is an attitude you must constantly strive to change. In science, right or wrong predictions don't matter. Science is the search for natural truths, and it matters not whether you come in the front door (correct predictions) or the back door (incorrect predictions) of the house of truth. What matters is that either way, in the end, you learn the truth.

Along with the development of this skill and this attitude must come the realization that certain predictions are more valid than others. A hypothesis is merely a guess, conjecture, or untested speculation. A theory is a higher level of prediction because it is an educated guess based on some evidence or past experience.

Designing/Experimenting

With the realization that speculation and prediction must be tested in controlled experiments to determine the truth, modern science was born. For too long, people accepted the musings of authority figures as truth and fact. Often the more bizarre the speculation, the more eager people were (and some still are) to believe it. Experimentation is what separates science from philosophy and superstition.

The practice of science enables scientists as ordinary people to go about doing generally ordinary things that, when assembled, reveal the extraordinary intricacies and awesome beauties of nature.
—Arthur Kornberg

The first hurdle to clear in experimental design is to determine what problem is to be solved. Problems should always be stated in question form, be as simple and specific as possible, and address only one factor at a time.

Let us use a whimsical imaginary problem to demonstrate experimental design. Suppose you had to solve the following problem: What is the effect on aardvarks of eating chocolate pudding? Assuming you had unlimited resources, your experimental design might go something like this:

Step 1
Determine what problem is to be solved. The problem—What is the effect on aardvarks of eating chocolate pudding?—is in question form, is specific, and deals with only one problem, so we are ready to proceed.

Step 2
Get 1,000 aardvarks. The more experimental subjects you work with, the more reliable is your data.

Step 3
Separate the aardvarks into two equal groups. In each group, put 500 aardvarks with the same age, sex, and physical characteristics. You want the two groups to be as nearly equal in all respects as possible.

Step 4
Keep both groups under identical conditions—same size cages, same amount and kind of food, same amount of water, same period of light and dark, same temperature, same humidity, and so on. These conditions, called the control variables, must be kept as nearly identical as possible.

Step 5
Feed one group of aardvarks chocolate pudding, and designate it the experi-

mental group. Do not feed chocolate pudding to the other group, and designate it the control group. The chocolate pudding in the experimental group is called the *manipulated variable*; it is the effect of this pudding that you are testing.

Step 6

Let the experiment run for a reasonable length of time. Collect appropriate data; for example, after two weeks the experimental group turns green and starts to do back flips.

Step 7

To verify these results, repeat the experiment as many times as possible with different aardvarks and different batches of pudding.

Step 8

Based on the accumulated data, draw reasonable conclusions. The reasonable conclusion here would be that apparently chocolate pudding causes aardvarks to turn green and do back flips.

Some problems are difficult or impossible to test experimentally. For example, to calculate the orbit of a comet, we would deduce certain outcomes then look to nature for verification.

The only solid piece of scientific truth about which I feel totally confident is that we are profoundly ignorant about nature.
—Lewis Thomas

Eliminating

Not only will you have to battle students' fear of making wrong predictions, you will also have to deal with students' fear of failure. Students must come to understand and believe that failure in science is not to be feared. Actually, we learn more from failure than success because failure raises more questions than success, and these questions, in turn, force even more inquiry. Science is dynamic and always changing. Newly discovered "facts" and even those laws of science that have withstood the test of time must be subject to revision at any moment. What we regard as facts are at best momentary illusions seen through a veil of ignorance. Today we laugh at the idea that earlier people thought it factual that the earth was flat or that living things could arise spontaneously from dead or inorganic matter. The future will show many of our so-called facts to be just as wrong.

It is possible that every law of nature so far has been incorrectly stated.
—J.B.S. Haldane

Students need to learn what data is appropriate to collect and how to organize data. Charting and graphing skills are essential. Organizing data into tables, charts, and graphs enables us to view the results in a graphic format. In this form, data is easier to understand and patterns are more easily discerned. Students must learn to deal with the fact that data may be "muddy"—inconsistent, unexpected, and often unfathomable.

Drawing Conclusions

What does the data mean? This is often difficult for professional scientists, let alone students, to answer. "Muddy" data can yield only "cloudy" conclusions, and students must learn to deal with this frustrating problem. Only experience will allow students to identify and support those conclusions that are valid and discard those that are not valid.

> *The art of becoming wise is the art of knowing what to overlook.*
> —William James

Once students have some proficiency in the skills aforementioned, they can begin to think scientifically and actually do science using the method illustrated below:

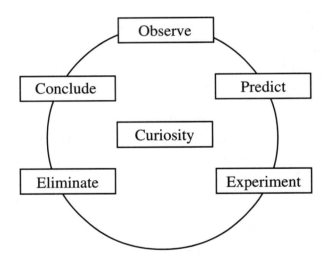

The scientific process is cyclic and becomes progressively more refined in view of the problem you are trying to solve.

Scientists approach problems in an organized way, but hunches and serendipity also play a role. What do Velcro, penicillin, x-rays, and Teflon have in common? Serendipity!—the lucky accident of finding valuable things not specifically sought after.

Science can be tedious, frustrating, and just plain boring with repeated failure often the

norm. It can also be the most challenging, stimulating, and rewarding thing a person can do. The only way for students to learn what science is and how it works is to let students actually <u>do</u> science.

> *Tell me, I forget*
> *Show me, I remember*
> *Involve me, I understand*
> —Chinese proverb

Dynamo Demos

The teacher-led Dynamo Demos (pp. 1–107) help students to develop the science process skills: observing, predicting, experimenting, eliminating data, and drawing conclusions. In addition, students develop their problem solving and creative/critical thinking skills.

In the Dynamo Demo activities, students do the thinking and the teacher does the doing. The teacher sets up and presents a "What will happen if...?" or "Why did that happen?" problem situation. Using guided questions and the necessary manipulation of apparatus and equipment, the teacher helps the students understand the problem, make accurate observations and reasonable predictions, and arrive at a conclusion or an answer to the problem.

While specific scientific principles and concepts are demonstrated in the Dynamo Demos activities, the primary focus is on actively involving students in the scientific process and developing problem solving and creative/critical thinking skills.

When possible, the Dynamo Demos are counterintuitive and present discrepant results. This approach makes the Demos more challenging and often results in incorrect predictions, forcing students to "come in the back door" to the truth.

The first demonstration is a preliminary activity designed to refine students' observation skills. The rest of the demonstrations can be done in any order.

> *We must not confuse the results of science with the ways in which scientists produce those results. The practice of science is a social process, an art or a craft and not a science.*
> —Michael Klapper

Creative Challenges

The student-centered Creative Challenges (pp. 108–48) help students develop their creative/critical-thinking, problem-solving, and "inventioneering" skills.

In the Dynamo Demos, the teacher sets up an experiment and uses select questions to guide the students to a solution of the given problem. With the Creative Challenges, the teacher presents the problem (challenge) then functions merely as a technical advisor. Students must design and develop a solution to the problem (challenge). This allows students to practice and apply the science process skills demonstrated in the Dynamo Demos.

The student combines a process of "solution generation" with trial and error to look for possible solutions to a given problem. Each time a possible solution is generated, the student must predict what will happen and then observe the results when the solution is implemented. Each solution that is tried requires analysis and interpretation of the results and allows the student to draw conclusions on how to best solve the original problem. Specific scientific principles and concepts are learned through the process itself rather than through direct teacher instruction.

> *"Discovery consists of seeing what everybody else has seen but thinking what nobody else has thought."*
> —Albert Szent-Gyorgyi

On Using This Book

The following are general information, guidelines, and hints for using this book:

- Use this book in conjunction with any commercial or teacher-authored science curriculum.

- The activities are designed to come from "left field." That is, the activities are not intended to teach any concept being discussed in class. The less the Demos and Challenges have to do with what is going on in class, the better. Students are then forced to think and create rather than turn to a book for the answer.

- The activities are not written to be formally graded. Assess and/or grade them as you see fit. I, personally, do not grade my students on the Demos or Challenges as I am not sure how you accurately evaluate and assess creativity and critical thinking. Furthermore, I worry that formal grading will stifle creativity and make these activities just another educational burden for students to endure.

- These activities produce creative effort and critical thinking, not marketable results. Failure and incorrect predictions are expected and even encouraged. Such is the reality of actual everyday science.

- Students should work individually as much as possible. If time and/or materials present a problem, students may work in design teams of two, preferably, but three if necessary. The larger the design teams, the less each team member will get from the activity and the more conflicts you will have within groups.

- Many of the challenges have a competitive element. Students need to be competitive and learn how to deal with competition; however, students should not lose sight of the fact that competition is secondary in these activities. Creative thinking and effort are the primary goals. Stress the process, not the product.

- Encourage students to do their own thinking and creating. Don't let competitive fervor lead to outside input by parents, siblings, and/or peers. Along those same lines, set spending limits on those challenges where students are required to supply their own construction materials.

- Try the activities before you present them to your class. The activities in this book are tried and tested, and I have attempted to write the directions in clear and concise terms. But play it safe, work things out beforehand. Don't waste precious class time by "winging it."

- You may want to ask students to submit a written explanation and drawings of the Creative Challenges before beginning. After using this process a few times, students should be able to handle the Challenges without the explanation and drawing.

- Once Demos and Challenges are complete, encourage students, when practical, to take this learning out of the classroom and share it with parents, siblings, and friends. This is what I call the "Ripple Effect." Educational research shows that we best learn what we teach to others. Always consider the safety, practicality, and the necessity of supervision when having students do these activities outside the classroom.

- Give students recognition for their efforts. This might include displaying their creations and inventions, awarding and displaying appropriate certificates of achievement, and/or presenting gag gifts as trophies. Such recognition will generate a great deal of student enthusiasm, parental support, and positive public relations.

- Kids may clamor to do these activities every day, but that is not the intent of this book. This book is designed to supplement an established curriculum. You should do one or two Demos first before starting students on the individual Challenges. There are enough Dynamo Demos in this book to do one demo every week and enough Creative Challenges to do one every other week during a normal-length school year. You certainly can do fewer than this, but in my experience, it may not be practical to do more from a time standpoint.

- Ask, don't tell. It is crucial that you help students develop their thinking skills by asking for student observations, predictions, and explanations rather than just giving the answer. Mix closed questions that demand factual recall with open questions that are divergent and thought-provoking. Use questions to generate discussion, but don't always call on the student who raises his hand, and give adequate wait time when you question. Space does not permit a detailed discussion here of how to construct good oral questions, but there are excellent resources available to help you develop sound questioning strategies.

In closing, be creative yourself with this book. Take my offerings and put your own twist to them. If you come up with a better way of doing some of the things in this book or with whole new activities that could be included in future editions of this book, contact me.

Dennis Holley
Critical Thinking Books & Software
P.O. Box 448
Pacific Grove, California 93950

Dynamo Demos

1   Stubborn Stuff

Problem: *Can we push the stuff down the tube/pipe and through the paper?*

Observe

1. In the space below, diagram and describe the system you see before you.

Predict

2. Predict what will happen when someone pushes the rod into the tube/pipe.

Conclude

3. What did happen when someone pushed the rod into the tube/pipe?

Predict

4. The teacher will now place some stuff (loose dry material) into the tube/pipe. Predict what will happen when someone pushes the rod into the tube/pipe.

Conclude

5. What did happen when someone pushed the rod into the tube/pipe after stuff had been added to it? Why did it happen that way?

1   For the Teacher

Objective

In this activity, students will determine why the teacher cannot push a small amount of stuff through a flimsy piece of tissue.

Materials Needed

- 1 tube or pipe (Exact size is not important. A piece about 1' to 2' long by 1/2" in diameter should work nicely. Exact composition of the tube/pipe is also not critical. Anything rigid—copper, steel, electrical conduit, glass, or plastic tubing should work. I prefer to use a rigid piece of plastic tubing so students can see what is happening on the inside of the system.)

- 1 rod or wooden dowel (The rod/stick should fit as snugly as possible into the tube/pipe and be 6" to 1' longer than the tube/pipe when fully inserted.)

- small rubber band

- several paper napkins, pieces of tissue, or sections of toilet paper

- small quantity of dry powdery material (Hereafter, "dry powdery material" will be referred to as "stuff." You should have enough stuff to fill the tube/pipe approximately half full. Any dry material should work as long as it is coarse. Sand, salt, or sugar will work.)

Curiosity Hook

Do some kind of manipulation with a tube or pipe and a rod as students enter the classroom. I place a tube on a rod, hold the rod on each end, and alternately raise and lower each end so that the tube slides along the rod.

Setup

1. Take a piece of paper—napkin, tissue, or toilet paper—and place it over one end of the tube. Fix it in place with a rubber band. The thinner the piece of paper, the more dramatic the effect. I like to use a single section of school toilet paper so thin you can practically see through it.

2. Insert the rod partway into the tube. Have students observe this system and write their description under 1 on the student page.

3. Ask students to hypothesize what will happen if someone continues to push the rod into the tube. Have them write their predictions under 2 on the student page.

4. Now ask a student (or do it yourself) to push the rod into the empty tube capped with a piece of paper on one end. They will easily push the rod through the paper cap. Have students write this result under 3 on the student page.

5. Now start over. Again place a piece of paper over one end of the tube and fix it in place with a rubber band. This time, add some stuff to the open end of the tube, filling it about half full.

6. Have students hypothesize what will happen now when someone pushes the rod into the tube. Have students write their predictions under 4 on the student page.

7. Ask a student (or do it yourself) to insert the rod into the open end of the tube and try to push the stuff out through the paper on the other end. Instruct them to push slowly but forcefully. Try as they might, the paper will never break. What's more, there won't even be a bulge in the paper. Have students write this result under 5 on the student page.

Safety Concerns

Use common sense.

Outcomes and Explanations

As someone pushes on the rod, the downward pressure on the stuff is immediately converted into a pressure that pushes the stuff in all directions equally. The harder they push on the rod, the more pressure there is with the stuff pushing out on the tube. They can never push the rod through the tissue. Have students write this explanation under 5 on the student page.

Application

Challenge students to further investigate.

Would using different stuff give different results? Would using a different size tube give different results? Would we get different results if we used a tube made of something different from what the first tube was made of? What if the size of the rod were smaller? larger?

Take Home

This activity can be easily and safely done by students outside the classroom. Encourage students to investigate the problems listed under the application section. They may spill sand, sugar, and/or salt, so caution them to conduct their experiments in a location where spills can be easily cleaned.

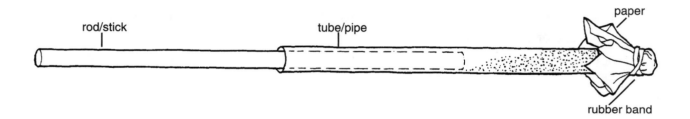

rod/stick   tube/pipe   paper   rubber band

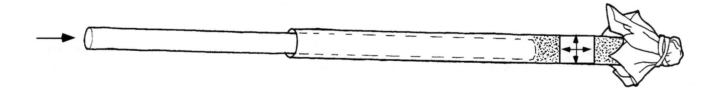

The Ever Amazing and Always Magnificent Water-Expanding Machine

Problem: *Is it possible to get more water out of a container than we put into it?*

Observe

1. In the space below, diagram and describe the system you see before you.

Predict

2. How much water is the teacher going to pour into the device? Predict how much water will come out of the device.

Conclude

3. How much water did come out of the device? If there is a discrepancy between how much water went in and how much came out, explain this discrepancy. In the space below, diagram how you think the inside of the water-expanding machine must look.

2 For the Teacher

Objective

In this activity, students will attempt to determine how a device appears to put out more water than was originally put into it in the first place.

Background Information

In science jargon, this activity is what is known as a "black box mystery." This phrase is used to describe situations where we attempt to understand how something works without being able to see the whole thing. The universe is the ultimate black box mystery. In this activity, students cannot see the inner workings of the device. They can only predict (guess) what is going on inside.

Materials Needed

- 1 cardboard box with a removable lid
- 1 two-liter plastic pop bottle
- short length of rubber or plastic tubing (3 feet should do it)
- cool glue gun with glue stick or a small quantity of silicon-based aquarium sealer
- small plastic or glass funnel
- catch container that will hold at least 3 times more than the pop bottle
- bricks or blocks to position the device above the catch container
- 1000 ml beaker or a 1-liter, plastic pop bottle

Curiosity Hook

I have the device sitting on a cart in the front of the room where my students can see it as they come in the door. On the front of the device (lid of the box), I have a sign that pro-

claims, "The Ever Amazing and Always Magnificent Water-Expanding Machine."

Setup

1. The diagrams illustrate how the completed device should look from both the outside and the inside. Ask students to observe and describe the device under 1 on the student page.

Outside View

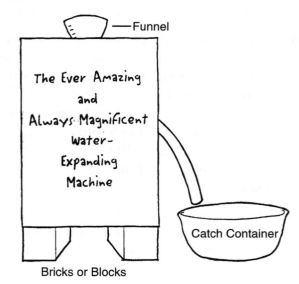

The Ever Amazing and Always Magnificent Water-Expanding Machine

Funnel

Catch Container

Bricks or Blocks

Inside View

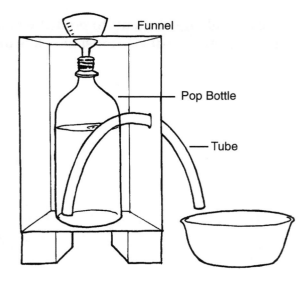

Funnel

Pop Bottle

Tube

2. Sealing the tube where it exits the pop bottle is not necessary other than to prevent leaks when the water level rises in the bottle as you add water to it. If you decide to seal the tube with a glue gun, use a cool glue gun (hot glue may melt the bottle). Rubbery clear silicon-based aquarium sealer will work to seal the tube as well. Under 2 on the student page, ask students to predict how much water will come out of the device.

3. Start with the level of the water in the pop bottle nearly up to the hole in the side of the bottle or nearly up to the level section of tube where it exits the bottle.

4. Begin by pouring about 1000 ml of water into a beaker or plastic pop bottle. Now begin pouring the water into the funnel on the device. After a portion of the measured water has been poured into the funnel, water should begin flowing out the tube into the catch container. The flow will stop only when the bottle inside is empty.

5. Once flow has stopped, begin pouring the water from the catch container back into the beaker or pop bottle you used to pour water down the funnel. You should get about 3 times as much water out as what you put down the funnel the first time.

6. Now challenge students to predict what the inside of the device must look like to get the results they have just witnessed. Have them put their predictions (diagrams) under 3 on the student page.

Outcomes and Explanations

As the water level inside the pop bottle rises, water begins running out the tube. This creates a siphon effect that doesn't stop until all or nearly all the water in the pop bottle has been siphoned off into the catch container.

Application

Challenge students to invent their own devices to amaze their friends and parents. Could they design and build a device that would have clear water going down the funnel but colored water coming out into the catch container? Or how about a device that would have clear water going down the funnel but a completely different liquid coming out into the catch container?

Take Home

This activity can be easily and safely done by students outside the classroom. Encourage students to investigate on their own the problems listed under the application section. They may spill water, so caution them to conduct their experiments in a location where spills won't be a problem.

Safety Concerns

Spilled water can be slippery.

3 The Hot Hand

Problem: *How close to the candle flame can the teacher safely get his/her hand?*

Observe

1. Describe what happens as the teacher lowers his/her hand closer and closer to the top of the candle flame. How close can the teacher safely come to the flame?

Predict

2. Predict what will happen when the teacher tries again with a piece of window screen just above the top of the flame.

Conclude

3. What did happen, and why did it happen that way?

3 For the Teacher

Objective

In this activity, students will use their powers of observation, prediction, and critical thinking to investigate how an ordinary piece of window screen can protect the teacher's hand from the heat of a candle flame.

Materials Needed

- 1 large candle and matches to light it

- 1 4" x 8" piece of metal window screen (Make sure you use metal screen and not the nylon type of screening. Fold the screen in half to get a double thickness and flatten it out as much as possible by tapping on it with a hammer.)

- safety glasses

- optional—lab/chemical thermometer that goes at least up to the boiling point of water—212° F or 100° C

Curiosity Hook

Have a lit candle positioned where students can see it as they enter the room.

Setup

1. Hold your hand about two feet above the candle flame and ask students to predict what will happen as you begin to lower your hand. Have students write their observations and predictions under 1 on the student page. You should be able to get your hand down to about two inches above the candle flame before you reach the serious pain zone. Be cautious when doing this and make sure to wear safety glasses.

2. You could also hold a thermometer above the candle at about the same height as you got your hand before yanking it away because of the heat/pain. The temperature shown on the thermometer will quickly rise. When the temperature gets to the boiling point, quickly remove the thermometer or you may "pop" it. This demonstration shows how hot the thermometer is only a short distance above the candle flame.

3. Now show students the window screen (I like to heighten the effect by pouring water through the screen). Ask students to predict what will happen when you hold the screen above the candle flame and then again lower your hand down on the flame. Have students write their prediction under 2 on the student page.

4. Hold the screen just at the tip of the flame with one hand and bring the other hand down to the flame. You should be able to get your hand nearly down to the screen without feeling much heat at all. While still holding the screen, you could bring the thermometer in to show how much lower the temperature is than before.

5. Challenge students to explain why your hand is not burned even though it is now extremely close to the flame. Have them write their explanations under 3 on the student page.

Safety Concerns

Use caution when lowering your hand down toward the flame. Wear safety glasses at all times when conducting this demonstration. Caution students not to try this at home.

Outcomes and Explanations

Metals are good conductors of heat. The screen conducts the heat away from the region of the flame, off into the air, and prevents it from rising up to burn you.

Application

Materials used to protect other things from overheating (in this case your hand) are called heat sinks. You could use the following things to show this effect in action: 1) Buy a small heat sink from an electronic store and explain how it is clipped on to transistors and other electronic parts when soldering them into circuit boards so that the heat buildup won't damage the transistors and electronic parts. 2) Take pictures of electrical transformers in your area showing the fins protruding from the housing to dissipate heat away from internal components. 3) Bring in a part of an old car radiator and show the large surface area created by the coil and metal leaves to conduct heat away from the engine.

Take Home

Since this activity involves open flame, great caution should be taken if students attempt this at home.

4 Wacky Water

Problem: *Will the water behave as we expect it to?*

Observe

1. In the space below, observe and describe the device the teacher has prepared.

Predict

2. Predict what will happen when the teacher pours water into the piece of hose sticking up in the air.

Conclude

3. What did happen, and why did it happen that way?

4 For the Teacher

Objective

This activity may drive you and your students to distraction because no one is totally sure why the water behaves the way it does in this one.

Materials Needed

- 1 one-gallon coffee can
- scrap piece of garden hose long enough to wrap around the coffee can 5-6 times
- small funnel
- beaker or cup to pour water with
- bucket or sink to catch the water

Curiosity Hook

Pour water into a straight piece of garden hose so the water is running out of the hose and into a sink or container as students enter the room.

Setup

1. Wrap the garden hose around the coffee can 5–6 times as shown. Under 1 on the student page, ask students to observe and describe the device.

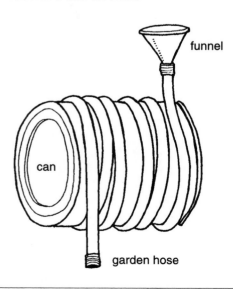

funnel

can

garden hose

2. Ask two students to hold the ends of the can. Insert the funnel into the portion of the hose sticking up in the air. Position the descending end of the hose over a bucket or sink. Now ask students to predict what will happen when you begin pouring water into the funnel. Have students write their predictions under 2 on the student page.

3. Now start pouring water into the funnel. Have students record their conclusions/explanations under 3 on the student page.

Safety Concerns

Be sure to wipe up any spills.

Outcomes and Explanations

If you set up the apparatus as described, the water will never come out of the lower end of the hose. You will reach a point where, as you add more water, it will simply overflow out of the tube end you are adding it to.

Why? No one knows for sure. I have seen it explained thusly:

"It is easy to figure out what happens for awhile. Water enters the upper tube and flows to the bottom where it rises to the same level as the water in the first descending tube. But once we reach the point shown in Figure A, what will happen next?

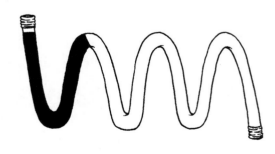

Figure A

Nine out of ten students, or teachers or world leaders for that matter, will say that as you add more water to the situation shown in Figure A, the water will spill over into the second descending column and the cycle will start over again until water drains out the end of the descending hose. This is not the case. As water is added, a column of water begins to pour over the first upper peak in the hose. But it does not simply dribble over the peak. As soon as the water seals off the first peak, additional water will begin a siphon. A siphon is an inverted u-shaped tube or pipe. When it is filled with enough water, the force of the liquid from a reservoir at one end will go over a barrier higher than the reservoir on the other end.

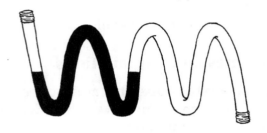

Figure B

The level in the section you are pouring water down will drop suddenly as the column of water siphons over into the second valley. The seeming paradox is not over yet. As wa-

ter is added from this point, the cycle will try to repeat itself. However, as water is now added, it will try to raise not one, but two columns of water. In effect, the section of hose that you add water to must be twice the height of the coffee can to create a force sufficient to raise both columns of water within the tube."

Application

This open-ended activity begs further investigation. Have students determine if the number of wraps of hose around the can influences the outcome—more wraps vs. less wraps. Some believe that it is possible to make water come out of the descending end of the hose if you raise the ascending portion of the hose. Does this work? Challenge students to check it out. To further student understanding, use clear tubing instead of hose and dye the water with food coloring.

Take Home

If students have the materials handy, encourage them to investigate this mystery further. Remind them to conduct their experiments where water spills will not be a problem. Who knows? You may have a bright student who can figure this out and explain it to the rest of us.

5 | Hindenburg II

Problem: *Will the balloon pop?*

Predict

1. Predict what will happen when the teacher tries to push the stick through the balloon.

Conclude

2. What did happen, and why did it happen that way?

5 For the Teacher

Objective

The seemingly impossible result of this activity will challenge your students' creative thinking skills in trying to explain it.

Background

This activity is named after the most famous balloon (dirigible) accident in history. The German dirigible *Hindenburg* was the largest rigid airship ever built. At 804 feet, the *Hindenburg's* hydrogen-filled air bags could lift nearly 473,000 pounds. Approaching the mooring at Lakehurst, New Jersey, on May 6, 1937, the dirigible burst into flame. The horrific pictures of the fiery blowup that killed 36 people aboard was the world's first view of modern aviation disasters. Your balloon certainly won't go up in flames (unless, perhaps, you fill it with hydrogen), and let's hope it won't pop as you skewer it.

Materials Needed

- 1 10- or 12-inch balloon
- 1 bamboo skewer 10–12 inches long (Usually, the smaller shishkabob skewers work well and are available at most grocery stores.)
- some cooking oil
- Note: I bought a kit called "Needle Thru The Balloon" from a magic supply company. The kit includes an extra large, extra heavy balloon and a huge (extra long) needle. Such kits may also be available from science supply companies that handle some novelty items.

Curiosity Hook

Toss small inflated balloons up and pop them with a pin as students enter the room.

Setup

1. Ahead of time, partially inflate (about half full) and tie off the balloon.

2. Hold up the balloon in one hand and the skewer in the other, and ask students to predict what will happen when you push the skewer through the balloon. Have students record their predictions under 1 on the student page.

3. Dip the skewer in the oil and gently twist and push the skewer through the thick nipple end of the balloon. Continue to gently twist and push until the skewer penetrates the knot end of the balloon and the point of the skewer emerges. As with any Dynamo Demo, it is best to practice this ahead of time as there is a bit of an art to it.

4. Have students write the result under 2 on the student page.

Safety Concerns

Skewer points are sharp, so be careful where you position your hands as you do this demo.

Outcomes and Explanations

1. Balloons are made of thin sheets of rubber latex which, in turn, are made of many long intertwined strands of polymer molecules. The rubber is stretchy because of the elasticity of the polymer chains. When the balloon is blown up, the polymer strands are stretched. The middle area of the balloon stretches more than the tied end and the nipple end (opposite the tie). A sharp, lubricated point can be pushed through the strands at the tie and nipple ends because the polymer strands will stretch around it. A sharp, lubricated point pushed through the

strands at the side of the balloon will pop (usually) because the strands are already stretched and will break. Once a tear begins, it enlarges as the air rushes out of the balloon.

2. Discuss the results with students and have them write the explanation under 2 on the student page.

Application

If time and student interest permits, consider these further investigations into the puzzle of polymers:

1. Does the size of the skewer matter? What is the smallest and/or largest thing you can skewer the balloon with and not have it pop?

2. Go for the record. As far as I can determine, the record for the most bamboo skewers in one balloon without popping is seven. Can you beat that?

Take Home

Challenge students to go home and find another polymer surface that they could also pierce with a sharp object without the surface leaking air or water (while the sharp object remains in the surface or container). Sandwich bags or freezer bags filled with water are good sources for home experimentation.

6 The Hungry Teacher

Problem: *How hungry can your teacher be? Is he/she hungry enough to eat a candle?*

Observe

1. Describe what you think you just saw.

Conclude

2. What actually happened?

3. What important point is the teacher trying to make?

6 For the Teacher

Objective

In science (and other aspects of life as well), careful observation is very important because often things are not as they appear to be. This demo is a good way to make this point clear to your students.

Materials Needed

- 1 large cork borer (about 1/2" to 3/4" in diameter)
- 1 large potato
- package of slivered almonds

Curiosity Hook

Eat something, like an apple, as students enter the room.

Setup

- Note: Do Step 1 ahead of time.

1. Force the cork borer through the potato to form a plug about 1/2"–3/4" in diameter and 3"–4" long. This will be your "candle." For the "wick," use a piece of slivered almond. Shave the almond down until it approximates the size of a candle wick. The oil in the almond will burn for several minutes once you light it.

2. Now light your "candle." Tell the students that you are so hungry that you could eat about anything, including the burning candle they see before them.

3. Blow out the candle and eat it (See Safety Concerns).

4. Have students describe what they think they just saw under 1 on the student page.

Safety Concerns

Caution: The almond may remain hot for several seconds.

Outcomes and Explanations

Explain to students the true nature of the "candle" and "wick." Have students write the explanation under 2 on the student page. This is a good time to impress on students how important careful observations are and how difficult it is to be a good observer. Have students write about the point you are making under 3 on the student page.

For a long time, people believed that the world was flat, the sun moved around the earth, frogs and fish were formed from mud, dead things generated flies, and many other false ideas we now know to be wrong. Were ancient peoples stupid? No, they were just ignorant and often careless observers. Hopefully, this demo will help students appreciate how often things are not as they appear in the world around them.

Take Home

Students can do this demo at home and help educate siblings, friends, and/or parents to the often deceptive nature of things around them. Impress on them the need to take caution with the open flame of the "candle."

7 Up in Flames

Problem: *Is it possible to boil water in a paper cup?*

Predict

1. Predict what will happen when the teacher heats paper container A with no water in it.

Conclude

2. What did happen when the teacher heated container A with no water in it?

Predict

3. Predict what will happen when the teacher heats paper container B with water in it.

Conclude

4. Did the water actually boil in container B? How can you tell?

Predict

5. How can we get container B to burn?

7 For the Teacher

Objective

Boil water in a paper container. Sound impossible? Students will think so until they use their powers of observation, critical thinking, and problem solving to discover that, with application of the proper scientific principles, even the seemingly impossible becomes feasible.

Materials Needed

- 2 paper containers (Most paper containers will work, but do NOT use Styrofoam or waxed paper cups as they will melt when heated even with water in them. To heighten the visual effect of this activity, I employ the very thin papers used to line cupcake pans. These papers can be purchased in any grocery store.

- 1 ring stand setup

- 1 heat source (You need an open flame so a hot plate will not work. A Bunsen burner setup works best, but if you don't have gas outlets in your room, a propane torch or an alcohol lamp will suffice.)

- safety goggles

Curiosity Hook

Have a beaker of colored liquid (food coloring in water) boiling on the ring stand when students come into the classroom.

Setup

1. Place an empty paper container (container A) on the ring stand but keep the flame off to one side. Tell students you are going to heat this paper container and ask them to predict the outcome. Students should write their prediction under 1 of the student page. Now move

the flame under the paper container. The empty paper container will begin to burn almost immediately. Have students record these results under 2 on the student page.

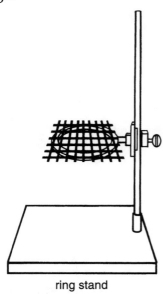

ring stand

2. Move the flame off to one side and place another empty paper container (container B) on the ring stand. This time put water in the paper container. Cupcake papers are very flimsy and tend to "relax" when heated so do not fill them completely. Again tell students you are going to heat this paper container, and ask them to predict the outcome. Students should write their prediction under 3 on the student page. Now move the flame under the paper container. The portion of the container above the water may char and even burn, but the portion of the container with water in it will not char or burn. In fact, in a few minutes, you will be actually boiling water in a paper cup. Ask students to answer questions 4 and 5 on the student page.

3. Keep the heat on container B until all the

water evaporates. Once the water has evaporated, container B will begin to burn.

Safety Concerns

1. Things will be bursting into flames in this activity so you need to wear safety glasses and keep students a safe distance away.

2. You will be working around an open flame, so be careful to keep clothes and hair away.

3. Position the ring stand so that it is not sitting on or near anything flammable.

4. Make sure any charred or burned pieces of paper discarded into the trash can are completely extinguished. More than one school fire has resulted from smoldering material in science room trash cans.

Outcomes and Explanations

1. Paper container A bursts into flame as expected because the heat from the flame causes the paper to quickly reach the kindling point (the temperature at which the paper catches fire).

2. Container B will not burn below water level although the paper above water level may char or burn. In a short time, the water in container B actually begins to boil. How can this be? The secret is heat transferal. The heat of the flame is trans-

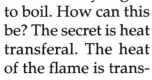
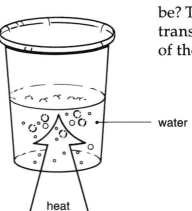

water

heat

ferred across the paper and into the water. This continues until the water temperature reaches the boiling point (100° C). The kindling point of the paper is above 100° C, so it will not burn as long as there is water in the container. However, once the water evaporates, the heat from the flame is absorbed only by the paper. Thus, container B reaches the kindling point and begins to burn.

Application

Have students apply what they have learned by imagining the following scenario: You (the student) are the owner of the Warm Night Wood Stove Company. One of your customers has come to you with a complaint. He/she says you sold and installed a defective stove because it takes a great deal of heat and a long time to get a fire started in the stove. What is the problem?

The information given indicates your company installed the stove. Assuming you knew what you were doing, the problem would not seem to be the stove. The problem probably lies with the wood being burned. If wood for a fireplace or stove is not cut and split so that it dries properly, it will contain a great deal of water (sap). As demonstrated with the paper container containing water, wet wood would have a higher kindling point than dry wood. The wet wood would necessitate a great deal of heat and time to dry the water (sap) out of it so the wood could finally ignite.

Take Home

Students should not attempt this activity at home. The flaming paper and scalding hot water produced in this demo present potential safety hazards.

8   Thing in a Bottle

Problem: *How did the teacher get that thing into that bottle?*

Observe

1. In the space below, diagram and describe the system you see before you.

Predict

2. How did the teacher get the device you see into the bottle? Obviously, the dowel can't be inserted into the bottle with a nail through it, and once a plain dowel is inserted into the bottle, a screw can't be placed through it.

Conclude

3. What is the explanation? How did the teacher get that thing into that bottle?

8 For the Teacher

Objective

Have you ever seen a sailing ship in a bottle? How do they do that? This activity will again make the point to students that things are not always as they appear and challenge them to use their creative thinking skills to figure out how you got that thing in that bottle.

Materials Needed

- 1 glass pop bottle

- 1 wooden dowel stick (The dowel should have a diameter just slightly smaller than the hole in the neck of the bottle.)

- 1 nail (Using a nail with a head on it will give a more dramatic effect and make the problem appear even more challenging. The length of the nail must be less than the diameter of the bottle.)

- several pieces of thread or very, very fine copper wire

Curiosity Hook

Have the device set up where students can see it as they enter the room.

Setup

- Note: Setup must be done before class time.

1. Begin by drilling a hole into the dowel just big enough for the nail to go through.

2. Next, tie a thread or fine copper wire around the pointed end of the nail.

3. Run the free end of the thread or wire through the hole in the dowel.

4. Gently allow some slack in the string or wire, and let the nail drop into the bottle.

5. Lower the dowel into the bottle, making sure that the thread or wire is still running from the point of the nail, through the hole, and out the bottle.

6. Now it is just a matter of pulling gently on the thread or wire to bring the point of the nail through the hole in the dowel.

7. By gently shaking the bottle, pulling the thread or wire, and a little good luck, you should be able to get the nail through the dowel. Once you have done this, simply pull hard on the string or wire to break it free from the nail. I prefer thin wire over thread or string since it comes free cleanly from the nail. If you use thread or string it may break and leave some on the nail, thus giving students a giant clue as to how you did it.

Safety Concerns

Use common sense in operating a drill; use caution with sharp nails.

Outcomes and Explanations

1. When finished, this intriguing device should appear as shown below. Students should observe and describe the device under 1 on the student page.

   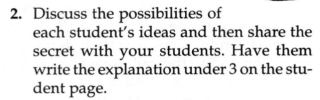

   Have students brainstorm as many ways as they can think of to explain how you got that thing into that bottle. Have them write their predictions under 2 on the student page.

2. Discuss the possibilities of each student's ideas and then share the secret with your students. Have them write the explanation under 3 on the student page.

Application

Challenge students to make some devices like this on their own. One challenge might be to duplicate what you have done except end with a screw in the dowel instead of a nail.

This feat can be accomplished by setting everything up the same. The only exception will be that you will use a small screw and wrap the thread or wire about 20 times around the head of the screw. By pulling on the thread or wire on the tip, you can start the screw into the hole in the dowel. A steady pull on the thread or wire wound around the head will turn the screw into the hole.

Take Home

Give students about a week to work on this challenge on their own. Then have them bring their devices to share with the rest of the class. You may be surprised at the weird things students try to get into a bottle (and hopefully, some of them succeed).

9 | Needle Through a Coin

Problem: *How did the teacher get that needle through that coin?*

Observe

1. In the space below, diagram and describe the situation you see before you.

Predict

2. How did the teacher get the needle into the coin? List as many ways as you can think of to explain what you see.

Conclude

3. What is the explanation? How did the teacher get that needle into that coin?

9 For the Teacher

Objective

The previous demo was designed to impress on students that things are not always as they appear. However, in this demo, things are exactly as they appear to be. This demo will challenge students to figure out how they got that way.

Materials Needed

- 2 needles
- 2 corks
- 1 hammer
- 2 coins (A dime works well for this activity, but any coin should do.)
- several blocks of wood to support the coin

Curiosity Hook

Have a coin with a needle through it positioned where students can see it as they enter the room.

Setup

- Note: Prepare one setup in advance. Complete the second during Step 3 of Outcomes and Explanations.

1. Arrange materials as shown in illustration.

2. There are two ways to pull this off. The first method is to take a small hammer, place the needle on the coin, and tap the needle very lightly for several hours. This works; it just takes a long time. The second method involves using pliers to force a needle nearly through a cork. A coin is laid down so that it is straddling two blocks of wood. The cork is set on the coin. When the needle is struck

smartly with a hammer, the coin will be pierced by the needle.

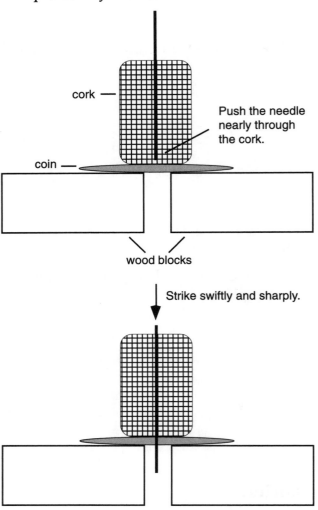

Safety Concerns

Wear safety goggles when hitting the needle embedded in the cork.

Outcomes and Explanations

1. Students should begin by observing and describing your curiosity hook setup. Descriptions should be recorded under 1 on the student page.

2. Now let students brainstorm as many ways as they can think of to explain how

you got the needle through the coin. These predictions should be entered under 2 on the student page.

3. Discuss the possibilities (and feasibility) of each student's ideas, and then share the secret with your students by showing them how to drive a needle through a coin. It's not magic, but simple physics, that makes this possible. The cork keeps the needle from bending and breaking when it is hit, directing all the energy to the tip of the needle. This directed force plus the speed at which the force is delivered allow the needle to penetrate the coin. Have students write the explanation under 3 on the student page.

Application

Ask students to envision this scenario: They have just emerged from an underground shelter after a tornado has passed. As they look at the devastation around them, they see shafts of wheat straw driven into trees like nails. Is this possible or just one of the myths that surround these catastrophic storms?

It is not only possible, but it does happen. In fact, there are documented cases of small tree branches no bigger than a pencil being driven into steel posts. How can this be? The answer is speed. When accelerated fast enough, even seemingly fragile objects become deadly penetrators. A grain of sand accelerated fast enough would blow a hole in a wall big enough to walk through. This is of great concern to NASA because even a small fleck of paint traveling at orbital velocity (nearly 18,000 m.p.h.) could be a deadly encounter if it were to strike an astronaut.

Take Home

I would be a little concerned about the safety factor of having students try this demo at home. Instead, suggest they try driving a piece of uncooked spaghetti through a potato. Like the needle through the coin, this seems impossible because of the fragile nature of the spaghetti, but it will work. Simply get one uncooked piece of spaghetti, hold it about in the center, and thrust it quickly into and through a small to medium raw potato. Here is one safety factor to consider: Watch where you position your hand on the other side of the potato or the spaghetti might skewer you as well as the spud.

10 The Thick and Thin Of It

Problem: *How thick is a piece of aluminum foil?*

Observe

1. Note the piece of aluminum foil being held by the teacher. Can you determine the thickness of this single piece of aluminum foil?

2. This is the only rule: You must indirectly measure the thickness of the foil. That is, you cannot use a measuring instrument to directly measure the thickness of the foil.

3. Write your solution to this problem in the space below.

10 For the Teacher

Objective

Can you determine the thickness of a piece of aluminum foil without being able to directly measure it? Students may throw their hands up in the air and say it's impossible, but with a little creative problem solving and a connection to things they may have learned in previous math or science courses, this problem can be solved.

Materials Needed

- 1 piece of aluminum foil to be used for the curiosity hook (I use a 1-foot square piece, but the exact size is not critical.)

- scales or a balance capable of measuring weight to at least the nearest tenth of a gram

Curiosity Hook

Idly manipulate a sheet of aluminum foil as students enter the room.

Setup

1. Show students the sheet of aluminum foil you were fiddling with as they entered the room. Ask them to reasonably estimate the thickness of the sheet. (Answers will probably vary greatly, indicating to students that no one actually has the slightest idea as to the thickness of a single sheet of aluminum foil.)

2. Now challenge students to determine the thickness of the sheet as precisely as possible. This is the only rule: They cannot use any measuring instrument to measure thickness directly. Some local indus-

try or university might have a precision measuring device that a student would have access to, thus eliminating the challenge of having to think through the problem.

3. I suggest you give your students some time (say several days to a week) to try and solve this problem. To add incentive, you might consider giving extra credit or bonus points to those students who do meet the challenge and solve the problem. Have students write their explanation under 3 on the student page.

Safety Concerns

Use common sense.

Outcomes and Explanations

1. There may be several alternate ways of solving this problem. Don't discount or discredit any student's solution. What we want to emphasize here is the thinking process, not necessarily the correct answer.

2. One possible solution would be to use the formula

$$\text{Density} = \frac{\text{mass}}{\text{volume}}$$

Determine the mass of the foil by weighing it (a 1-foot square piece of foil weighs about 4.3 g [0.14 oz.]). Then find the density of aluminum in a reference book. With this information, the volume of the piece of foil can be discerned. Once the volume, length, and width of the piece is known, you should be able to calculate the thickness.

11 Fireballs in the Sky

Problem: *What causes the fireball?*

Predict

1. Predict what will happen when the teacher sprays the candle flame with a stream of flammable material.

Conclude

2. What did happen when the teacher sprayed the candle flame with a stream of flammable material?

Predict

3. Predict what will happen when the teacher sprays the candle flame with a mist of flammable material.

Conclude

4. What did happen when the teacher sprayed the candle flame with a mist of flammable material?

5. Alcohol is highly flammable. Explain the results of the two experiments. Why did each experiment happen the way that it did?

11 For the Teacher

Objective

The dictionary defines the word flammable as "capable of being easily ignited and of burning quickly." However, as this activity will show, the form of the flammable material has a lot to do with the degree of flammability.

Materials Needed

- 1 meter or yardstick

- 1 candle (Exact size is not critical, but birthday candles are too small to produce a dramatic fireball.)

- spray bottle (The nozzle on the spray bottle should be adjustable to produce a stream and a mist.)

- about 50 ml of denatured alcohol (Rubbing alcohol will work.)

Curiosity Hook

Have a little alcohol burning in a small shallow glass container (such as a watch glass) as students enter the room. The flames of alcohol burn nearly colorless, so you may want to turn the room lights off to heighten the effect.

Setup

1. Ahead of time, light a candle and use the hot wax to attach the candle to one end of a meter stick.

2. Talk to students about the burning alcohol setup from the Curiosity Hook. Make sure they understand the concept of flammability.

3. Now, light the candle on the meter stick and have students predict what will happen when you shoot a stream of flam-

mable alcohol through the candle flame. Have students write their predictions under 1 on the student page. Hold the spray bottle about 3–4 inches from the flame, and shoot a quick stream of alcohol through the flame perpendicular to the top of the candle wick. Very little, if any, of the stream should ignite. Have students write the results under 2 on the student page.

4. Adjust the spray pattern on your spray bottle so it will spray a fine mist. Ask students to predict what will happen when you shoot a fine mist through the candle flame. Have students write their predictions under 3 on the student page. Again hold the spray bottle about 3–4 inches from the flame, and shoot a quick mist of alcohol across the candle flame. You should get a nice but brief fireball. Have students write the results under 4 on the student page.

Safety Concerns

1. Wear safety glasses.

2. Do not use hair spray or any flammable mousse, oil, or tonic on your hair the day you plan to do this demo, or you may become a fireball, too.

3. Position students well back, and do not spray the alcohol mist toward anything flammable.

Outcomes and Explanations

1. For anything to burn, three requirements must be met: 1) a fuel source, 2) oxygen to support combustion, and 3) a temperature above the ignition point of the fuel. Highly flammable materials have low ignition temperatures.

2. When you spray a thick stream of alcohol through the candle flame, it will not ignite because it does not remain in the flame long enough to reach ignition temperature.

3. However, when you spray a mist of alcohol onto the flame, you have broken the alcohol down into many tiny droplets. The droplets move slowly enough to reach ignition temperature at the same time, resulting in a fireball. Discuss this with students, and have them write the explanation under 5 on the student page.

Application

During the Gulf War in 1991, our military forces used fuel air bombs that work on the same principle as illustrated in this demo. Once released from an airplane, a fuel air bomb begins to rapidly emit a very fine mist of a gasoline-type hydrocarbon mixture. Upon ignition of the bomb, all the tiny droplets ignite simultaneously, producing an explosion. The explosion exceeds that produced by a small tactical nuclear weapon. These bombs were set off above mine fields. The pressure on the ground below was so great that buried mines were detonated, clearing the way for ground troops to safely walk.

Take Home

It is not safe for students to be making fireballs in their homes and garages. I suggest you strongly discourage students from repeating this demo at home.

12 The Amazing Drinking Bird

Problem: *Is the bird really drinking?*

Observe

1. Observe and diagram the situation you see before you.

Conclude

2. Is the bird really drinking? Explain what is happening.

12 For the Teacher

Objective

This is another situation in which things are not exactly as they seem to be. Students will have to use their powers of observation and critical thinking to determine what causes the drinking bird to continually dip its head in the water.

Materials Needed

- 1 "drinking bird" device (These are relatively inexpensive and can be purchased at novelty shops or from scientific supply companies.)

- beaker or cup of water (A 250 ml beaker or cup about 3.5" tall and full of water will allow the device to "drink" freely. You may want to use distilled water [tap water may leave mineral residue on the head of the "bird" when it dries]).

- optional—a small fan

Curiosity Hook

Have the device set up and working where students can see it as they enter the classroom.

Setup

1. Shortly before class begins, start the device "drinking." Dip the head of the "bird" into the container of water so that the head is thoroughly saturated with water. Then place the device next to the container of water so the "beak" dips into the water when the "bird" bends over.

2. I find the device works better if I place a small fan nearby to blow air over it.

Safety Concerns

These devices contain a type of refrigerant that could be harmful if swallowed. However, unless the device gets broken, there is no danger of that.

Outcomes and Explanations

Ask students to observe and, under 1 on the student page, diagram the drinking bird. As water evaporates from the top end (head) of the device, cooling occurs. Cooling the top end lowers the pressure inside the top bulb. Higher pressure in the lower bulb then begins to push the colored liquid in the device from the lower bulb up through the tube and then to the upper bulb. Eventually, this moving liquid causes a shift in the center of gravity. The "bird" bends over and appears to drink by putting its "beak" in the container of water. When the device bends, an air bulb travels up the tube into the upper bulb, equalizing the pressure. The liquid flows back down into the lower bulb, and the "bird" stands up. Since the "bird's" head got wet when it "drank," the whole process starts again. Have students write this explanation under 2 on the student page.

Positioning a small fan so that it blows air over the device will improve performance by increasing the evaporation rate.

Application

Challenge students to invent ways of using this process and device in a practical manner. I'm not sure a giant drinking bird could be used to pump oil, but many of the things we take for granted today were also considered impractical when they were first proposed.

13 | Long Board, Short Board

Problem: *Which board will hit the floor first?*

Observe

1. In the space below, diagram and describe the system you see before you.

Predict

2. Predict which board will hit the floor first when the teacher releases both boards at the same time.

Conclude

3. Which board did hit the floor first? Explain why it happened that way.

Predict

4. Predict which bat will hit the floor first when both are released at the same time.

Conclude

5. Which bat did hit the floor first? Why did it happen that way?

13 For the Teacher

Objective

Although some people still have a hard time accepting it, Galileo demonstrated that two objects of different weights, when released together, will strike the ground at the same time.

If we conclude that Galileo's rule of falling bodies holds true, then it seems only natural to assume that two objects of the same weight when released together would also strike the ground at the same time. However, in this activity, students will be challenged to reason why this is not always true.

Materials Needed

- 2 boards (A three-foot-long piece of 2 X 4 and a two-foot-long piece of 2 X 4 will work nicely. Exact dimensions are not critical, but the boards should be of the same type of wood and of the same width. The only variable should be the length of the boards.)

- 2 baseball or softball bats (The bats must be the same length and made of the same material. Don't use one wood and one aluminum bat or this may not work.)

Curiosity Hook

Stand one board upright on the floor and drop it as students enter the room.

Setup

1. Stand both boards upright on the floor and lean them forward a little (away from you). Ask students to observe and describe the system you have created. Under 1 on the student page, have students diagram and describe what they're seeing.

2. Now ask students to predict which board will hit the floor first when you release both of them at the same time. Have students write their predictions under 2 on the student page.

3. Release the boards at the same time. Discuss the outcome and have students write their explanations under 3 on the student page.

4. Now stand two bats upright on the floor, one with the handle up and the other with the handle down. Lean the bats forward a little. Ask students to predict which bat will hit the floor first when they are released at the same time. Have students write their prediction under 4 on the student page.

5. Release the bats at the same time. Discuss the outcome and have students write their explanations under 5 on the student page.

Safety Concerns

Watch out for those dreaded splinters!

Outcomes and Explanations

1. The shorter the board, the faster it will fall. A physicist would explain this by saying that the rotational inertia of an object (our boards) is proportional to the mass of the objects and to the square of the length of the object (assuming the boards are of uniform composition). In layman's terms, the short board hits first because it rotates faster. Have students write this explanation under 3 on the student page.

2. So then the mass of an object and the length of an object are involved with its rate of fall. Again, however, there is more to it than that. The falling bats demonstrate that the distribution of the mass

in relation to the point of rotation is also critical.

Application

Ask students to apply what they have learned by answering this question: Why do ice skaters spin faster when they pull their arms in?

A physicist would say that as the skater pulls his/her arms in after beginning to rotate, the moment of inertia decreases. To conserve angular momentum, the angular velocity must increase. In other words, by pulling in the arms, the skater has changed the distribution of his/her mass in relation to the point of rotation. This change in the distribution of mass causes the skater to spin faster. This is also why divers can do more rotations in the tuck position than in the layout position.

14 Flaming Presidents

Problem: *Does the teacher really have money to burn?*

Observe

1. What did the teacher soak the money in?

Predict

2. Predict what will happen when the teacher tries to set the money on fire.

Conclude

3. What did happen when the teacher tried to set the money on fire? Explain why it happened that way.

14 For the Teacher

Objective

In this activity, students will use their powers of observation and critical thinking to understand why the money does not go up in flames.

Materials Needed

- small amount of rubbing alcohol and water mixed one to one

- dollar bill (Larger denominations will generate more student interest.)

Curiosity Hook

Partially or totally darken the classroom before students come in. As students enter, light a small piece of dry paper (such as newspaper) on fire. Wear safety glasses when doing this, and hold the burning paper with tongs over a fireproof container such as a sink.

Setup

1. Let students observe you soaking a piece of paper money in the alcohol/water mixture. Do not reveal what the liquid consists of. Have students answer question 1 on the student page.

2. Ask students to predict what will happen when you try to set the soaked paper bill on fire. Students should write their predictions under 2 on the student page.

3. Now hold the wet bill with tongs over a fireproof container and light it with a match. Wear safety glasses when doing this. The money will burn briefly and then go out. Alcohol does not produce a highly visible flame when it burns so doing this part in a partially or totally darkened room will heighten the effect.

Safety Concerns

1. Make sure all flammable materials and students are well away from your demo area.

2. Make sure you don't have any flammable hair spray, mousse, or gel in your hair that could catch fire.

3. Wear safety glasses at all times.

4. Handle burning paper with tongs.

5. Hold burning paper over a fireproof container.

Outcomes and Explanations

As the alcohol burns, it heats the water. The water then evaporates, carrying away heat with it. This process removes heat fast enough to prevent the paper from reaching ignition temperature. As more and more alcohol burns away, more water is left behind, and the flame will finally go out without harming the bill (except for it being a little soggy). Have students write this explanation under 3 on the student page.

Application

This same principle keeps humans from overheating. As sweat evaporates from the skin, it carries heat with it, preventing us from reaching fatally high temperatures.

Take Home

Alcohol is highly flammable. I suggest you strongly discourage students from repeating this demo at home.

15 The Cling Effect

Problem: *Why do the water streams cling together? What is the Cling Effect?*

Observe

1. In the space below, diagram and describe the system you see before you.

2. How did the teacher get the streams of water to cling together?

Conclude

3. Why do the streams of water cling together?

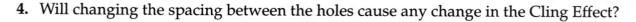

Predict

4. Will changing the spacing between the holes cause any change in the Cling Effect?

Conclude

5. What is the relationship between the spacing of the holes and the Cling Effect?

Predict

6. Will changing the amount of water in the container cause any change in the Cling Effect?

Conclude

7. What is the relationship between the amount of water in the container and the Cling Effect?

15 For the Teacher

Objective

In this activity, students attempt to determine the cause of the Cling Effect.

Materials Needed

- 2 empty milk cartons or plastic pop bottles

- something round and sharp to make holes in the container (A metal school compass or a scratch awl works well for this.)

Curiosity Hook

Have a container of water with a single stream of water flowing out of it and into a sink or container. Set it up where students can see it as they enter the classroom.

Setup

1. Punch three small holes in one of the sides near the bottom of a milk carton or plastic pop bottle. The holes should be about 1/2 cm from each other in a straight horizontal line.

2. Have students observe the container with holes in it. Have students write/diagram their observations under 1 on the student page.

3. Fill the container about 1/2 full of water. Have students observe the water streams coming out of the holes.

4. Bring the streams together with your fingers to make it one big stream. Have students describe this under 2 on the student page.

5. Have students discuss what causes the water streams to cling together. Have students write their explanation under 3 on the student page. Separate the large stream back into small streams by pushing one finger through the middle of the large stream. It may take several attempts to separate them.

6. Now have students predict if changing the spacing between the holes will cause any change in the Cling Effect. Have students write their predictions under 4 on the student page.

7. In the second container, punch three holes in the same approximate location and of the same approximate size as the first container, but space them about 1 cm apart.

8. Fill the container 1/2 full of water and attempt to bring the streams together. Have students discuss the relationship between the spacing of the holes and the Cling Effect. Have students write their explanations under 5 on the student page.

9. Will changing the amount of water in the container cause a change in the Cling Effect? Have students write their predictions under 6 on the student page.

10. Fill the first container full of water. Try to bring the streams together and then separate them. Empty the first container and fill it only half full. Try to bring the streams together and then separate them. Do the same with the second container. Have students discuss this and then write their explanation under 7 on the student page.

Safety Concerns

Be sure to clean up any spills.

Outcomes and Explanations

1. Water molecules attract each other through a process called cohesion. When you bring the streams of water together with your fingers, the cohesive forces between the water molecules are great enough to hold the streams together in a single stream. Have students write this explanation under 3 on the student page.

2. What is the relationship between the spacing of the holes and the Cling Effect? The closer the holes, the easier it is to get a single stream, but the harder it is to separate it back into individual streams. The opposite should be true for holes spaced farther apart. Have students write this under 5 on the student page.

3. What is the relationship between the amount of water in the container and the Cling Effect? The fuller the container, the greater the pressure, and the easier it is to separate streams. With less water and thus lower pressure, it is easier to form one cohesive whole stream. Have students write this under 7 on the student page.

Application

One example of the Cling Effect can be found in a shower head with many holes in it. When the valve is turned wide open, separate streams are produced, but when the valve is only partially opened, the many small streams will cling together and form one whole stream.

Take Home

Does the size of the holes make a difference? Does the orientation of the holes—vertical rather than horizontal—make a difference? Challenge students to investigate these questions further at home.

16 Tipsy Tumblers Trick

Observe

1. Watch as the teacher shows you a simple trick involving three tumblers (glasses). The rules are as follow:

   A. You have to turn over two tumblers at a time.

   B. You can make only three total inversions.

   C. There is absolutely no talking.

Predict

2. Now that you have seen the trick, can you do it?

Conclude

3. What is the real trick here?

16 For the Teacher

Objective

This activity will challenge your students' abilities to make careful observations.

Materials Needed

- 3 identical tumblers or glasses (I prefer plastic ones so they don't break if dropped.)

Curiosity Hook

Toss one of the tumblers up in the air, and catch it as students enter the room.

Setup

1. Begin by challenging students to repeat the Tumbler Trick you will show them.

2. Establish these rules before you show them the trick (Refer students to 1 on the student page):

   A. You must invert two tumblers at a time.

   B. You can make only three inversions.

   C. There is absolutely no talking. (You don't want someone who observes what is going on to give it away to the others.)

3. Start with the tumblers as shown below:

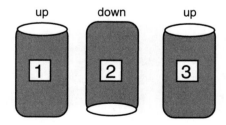

4. Make all inversions quickly so students have somewhat of a hard time following what you do. You may want to practice the inversions step-by-step ahead of

time so you can perform them quickly and smoothly.

5. Inversion #1—Grab glass 1 with one hand and glass 2 with the other, inverting them quickly into the arrangement shown below:

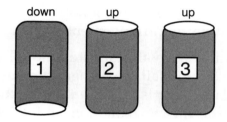

6. Inversion #2—Quickly grab glasses 1 and 3, and invert them to end up with the arrangement show below:

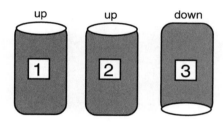

7. Inversion #3—Finally grab glasses 1 and 2 and quickly invert them simultaneously so that all three glasses are now upside down. Trick accomplished!

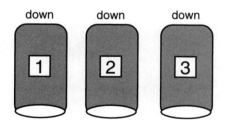

8. Now for the real trick. Ask for a volunteer. Challenge him/her to repeat the trick you just did within the rules previously established. Ask the rest of the class to predict, under 2 of the student page, whether the volunteer can do the trick. As the student volunteer is coming for-

ward, set the tumblers up; but rather than starting as you did with the center one down, set the center tumbler up and the two outside tumblers down.

9. Usually no one will notice that you have arranged the starting position of the tumblers differently. Add one more rule before the student volunteer begins. Tell them they have only 30 seconds to repeat your trick. This will fluster them into working fast and not noticing the different starting arrangement of the tumblers.

10. Allow several more student volunteers to try and fail. Challenge students to explain what is going on. Have students write their explanation under 3 on the student page.

Safety Concerns

If you are using glass tumblers, be careful not to drop them.

Outcomes and Explanations

The real trick is that, with this changed starting arrangement, there is no way to repeat the trick within the rules previously agreed on. Only those students who make careful and complete observations will be able to determine why you alone can perform the trick. Make sure that those students who see what is happening don't blurt out the answer to the others.

Take Home

This is an excellent activity for students to use to impress on their parents, siblings, and friends the necessity of careful observation.

17 Brain Games

Problem: *Can your C.O.B.U. (Corporation of Brains Unlimited) team solve the challenge it has been given?*

Procedure

1. C.O.B.U. teams will be established.

2. Each team will draw a challenging task they must perform within a set time limit.

3. At the end of the time limit, each team will report their findings, explanations, and/or conclusions to the rest of the class.

Good luck and may your neurons live long and prosper!

17 For the Teacher

Objective

This activity will challenge your students to (1) brainstorm about difficult problems (2) work together as a team and (3) communicate their ideas and conclusions to the rest of the class.

Materials Needed

- paper
- large container

Setup

- Note: Step 1 must be completed ahead of time.

1. Write 10–20 tasks or challenges on slips of paper for student groups, and place them into a large container. The following is a list of possible tasks/challenges you might present to students:

- What was the single most significant event of this century?

- Invent a color.

- Think of 5 things to do with soil besides agriculture.

- Invent an improved something (mousetrap, tennis racquet, etc.).

- Describe what it would feel like to be a something (tree, mountain, etc.).

- Bring in 5 examples of past, present, and future from school grounds.

- Explain whether you would rather be a robin that is afraid to fly or a fish that is afraid to swim.

- Decide which is more powerful—a weed or a stone wall and why.

- List 5 impossibilities.

- Explain which would last longer—an igloo in the desert or a caterpillar on a highway.

- Explain gravity.

- Explain what you would do if you could become invisible.

- Prove that you were not created 5 minutes ago complete with memories.

- If a tree falls in the forest and no one is there, is there a sound? Defend your answer.

2. Divide the class into groups. I call them C.O.B.U. (Corporations of Brains Unlimited) teams. You can let the students pick their own teams or you can assign them. I recommend two- or three-member teams because the larger the team, the less input each student will have.

3. Have one member from each team draw for a specific task or challenge the group must perform.

4. Once students have drawn their task/challenge, give them a time limit in which to complete it. The shorter the time limit, the more challenging the activity but the lower the quality of student work.

5. Once the time limit is up, have each team present their findings, explanations, or conclusions to the rest of the class.

Safety Concerns

None

Take Home

Encourage students to take these tasks/challenges home and discuss them with their parents, siblings, and friends. A deep philosophical discussion every now and again can do amazing things for the intellectual development of everyone involved.

18 Playing the Pipes

Problem: *Without taking a night class in playing the bagpipes, is there a way to play a twirling tube?*

Observe

1. In the space below, diagram and describe what the teacher is doing.

Conclude

2. What causes the eerie sound produced by the twirling tube?

Predict

3. Is there a relationship between the speed at which we swing the tube and the sound that the tube produces?

Conclude

4. What is the relationship between the speed of the tube and the sound produced?

18 For the Teacher

Objective

In this activity, students will determine the cause of the eerie sounds produced by the twirling tube.

Materials Needed

- a section of corrugated tube, approximately 3 feet long, with a 1-inch inside diameter (Some science demo books instruct you to use a vacuum cleaner hose, but I have not had much success with it. I recommend purchasing plastic tubes especially made for this purpose. These tubes may be purchased at a nominal expense from toy stores, novelty shops, and some science supply companies.)

Curiosity Hook

Twirl the tube (not so fast as to make a sound) or blow into it as students enter the room.

Setup

1. Twirl the tube just fast enough to make a sound. Under 1 on the student page, have students describe what you did and the sound produced. Ask them to write what they think caused the eerie sound under 2 on the student page.

2. Now ask students to predict if there is a relationship between the speed at which we twirl the tube and the sound the tube produces. Have students write their predictions under 3 on the student page.

3. As you twirl the tube faster and faster you will hear different and succeedingly higher pitches.

Safety Concerns

Be careful not to hit students or yourself as you twirl the tube around.

Outcomes and Explanations

1. This is an application of Bernoulli's principle. As the free end of the tube passes through the air, the air pressure within the tube is reduced. Because of this lower internal pressure, air rushes into the tube at the bottom. You can demonstrate this by holding the bottom of the tube stationary above a few small pieces of torn paper. As you twirl the upper part of the tube, the pieces of paper will come flying out the top of the tube. As the air moves through the tube, it begins to oscillate because of the corrugations of the tube (so a smooth tube won't work). The corrugations determine the frequency of the oscillation and thus the tone produced. Have students write this explanation under 2 on the student page.

2. There is a relationship between the speed of the tube and the sound produced. At slower speeds, the oscillations are slower (lower frequency) and a basic low tone is heard. As the tube moves faster, oscillations increase and the pitch rises. The next tone heard will be at a frequency twice the one before, or one octave higher. No intermediate tones will be heard at intermediate velocities. Have students write this explanation under 4 on the student page.

Application

Flutes and piccolos produce their sound by this same principle. A person playing one of these instruments blows across the hole in one end of the instrument rather than into the instrument. Perhaps one of your students plays one of these instruments in the school band or orchestra and could demonstrate for the rest of the class.

19 Moby Grape

Problem: *Can the teacher make grapes act like whales, diving and rising?*

Observe

1. In the space below, diagram and describe the system the teacher has prepared.

Predict

2. Predict what will happen to the grapes when they are both dropped into the carbonic ocean.

Conclude

3. What did happen when the grapes were dropped into a carbonated liquid, and why did it happen that way?

19   For the Teacher

Objective

In this activity, students will attempt to determine why one grape rises but the other doesn't.

Materials Needed

- several grapes, half peeled and half not peeled.

- container of clear carbonated liquid (Plain carbonated water or clear pop will work. You can also use a seltzer tablet in a glass of water.)

Curiosity Hook

You can catch students' attention and a little snack for yourself by eating some of the grapes as the students enter the classroom.

Setup

- Note: Complete Step 1 ahead of time.

1. Shortly before class begins, peel several grapes. Rinse the peeled grapes and an equal number of unpeeled grapes in water and place them on a towel.

2. Once the class is seated and attentive, open a container of carbonated beverage and pour it into a clear container placed where the class can see it. Or pop a seltzer tablet into a clear container of water. Hold up one of each type of grape. Have students observe this situation and write their descriptions under 1 on the student page.

3. Explain that you are going to drop several peeled and unpeeled grapes into the carbonated liquid. Ask students to predict what will happen, and have them write their predictions under 2 on the student page.

4. Drop the grapes into the liquid.

Safety Concerns

Use common sense; spilled grapes can make the floor slippery!

Outcomes and Explanations

The bubbles forming in the carbonated liquid are carbon dioxide gas. These bubbles will attach to the unpeeled grape but not the peeled grape. Why? The unpeeled grape has water-repelling (hydrophobe) properties, and thus, the CO_2 bubbles can adhere to its surface. The peeled grape is hydrophyl (water-attracting) and the bubbles of CO_2 have no place to attach. As the bubbles accumulate on the unpeeled grape, it eventually becomes light enough to float. Have students write this explanation under 3 on the student page.

Take Home

This activity can be easily and safely done by students outside the classroom. Encourage students to investigate whether other objects will demonstrate this same effect.

20 The Foo Can

Problem: *How can we put water in the can but get no water back out of the can?*

Observe

1. In the space below, diagram and describe the system you see before you.

Predict

2. The teacher will now pour some water into the can and then turn the can over. Predict what will happen when the teacher inverts the can.

Conclude

3. How can you explain what did happen when the teacher inverted the can?

20 For the Teacher

Objective

Demo 2, The Ever Amazing and Always Magnificent Water-Expanding Machine, presented students with the challenge of understanding how water can seemingly expand. In this demo, students are presented with the problem of water that seems to disappear.

Demo 20 is what is known as a "black box mystery" because students cannot see the inside of the device, only predict its inner design. This demo allows students to see into the device but with the inner design partially hidden. Not only are students challenged to explain the device but the opportunity can again be taken to make the point that things are not always as they appear. Only through careful observations and logical thought can we learn the truths of the universe.

Background Information

It is called the Foo can, but I have no idea why. They have been used for centuries by magicians to make a sample of liquid disappear.

Materials Needed

- 2 empty cans with the lid removed and the inside thoroughly cleaned (The template shown will fit a 28 oz. can. The second can is used for the Curiosity Hook.)

- thin piece of metal large enough to hold the template (A lid from the large stock cans of soup or vegetables used in the school cafeteria will work nicely.)

- metal shears

- black spray paint

- hot glue gun

Curiosity Hook

Pour water from one container to another as students enter the room.

Setup

1. Prepare the Foo can ahead of time according to the following directions:

    A. Spray paint the inside of the can with flat black paint. You could also paint the outside of the can and perhaps attach a label.

    B. Copy the template, cut it out, and tape it to the large can lid.

    C. Use the metal shears to cut the lid in the shape. Cut off and discard the lower part of the metal oval as marked on the template.

    D. Spray paint the front and back of the metal oval with flat black paint.

    E. Hot glue the oval into the can as shown below. Keep the oval at least one inch below the top of the can so students will not be able to see it when you show them the inside of the can. Use the least amount of glue possible so that students cannot see the glue joints.

    F. Give the insides of the can one more shot of spray paint, especially the glue joints.

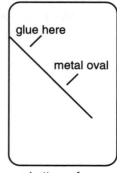

2. Show students the outside of the can, and then tip the can toward them and show them the inside of the can. I sug-

gest you do this at some distance from the students so they do not get a close view, especially of the inside of the can. Have students record their observations under 1 on the student page.

3. Now pour a measured amount of water into the Foo can. I suggest you practice ahead of time so you know exactly how much water to add and how to tip the can so that the water runs in behind the glued oval and not out onto the floor. Ask students to predict what will happen when you turn the can upside down. Have students record their predictions under 2 on the student page.

4. Turn the can upside down in such a manner that the water runs in behind the glued oval. You should now be standing in front of the class with the can totally inverted but no water coming out.

5. To show students that the water is still there, turn the can right side up. Now turn the can upside down again but in such a manner that the water runs out into a sink or container and not down behind the glued oval.

6. Have students brainstorm and discuss the explanation for what they have just seen. Have students record their explanations under 3 on the student page. Reveal the secret by passing the Foo can around and/or diagramming the interior structure of the can.

Outcomes and Explanations

The angle at which you tip the can determines whether the water will remain in the can, be caught by the metal template, or run out the opening on top.

Safety Concerns

Be careful of the sharp metal edges as you construct the Foo can.

Take Home

Encourage students to construct their own Foo can and use it to challenge the observation and logical thinking skills of their parents, siblings, and friends.

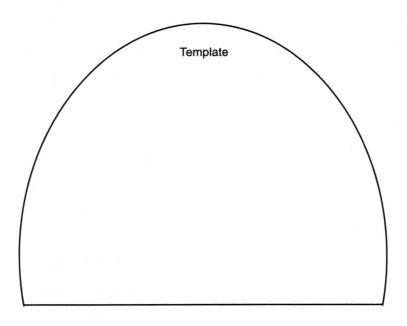

Template

21 Chemistry Connections

Problem: *Can you find all this stuff?*

Observe

A. Take this sheet with you to a grocery store. Try to find products with the following ingredients listed on the label. Write the product name beside the name of the chemical.

B. You will be awarded one point for each product you identify that contains a chemical on the list. The teacher will tell you how long you have to meet this challenge.

1. pyrethrins:
2. gum arabic:
3. ammonium lauryl sulfate:
4. phosphoric acid:
5. methyl salicylate:
6. EDTA:
7. potassium citrate:
8. gum acacia:
9. cetyl alcohol:
10. carrageenan:
11. nitrous oxide:
12. xanthan gum:
13. Americum-241
14. cyanoacrylate:
15. xylene:
16. piperonyl butoxide:
17. polysorbate 80:
18. urea:
19. aluminum zirconium:
20. quinine:
21. brominated vegetable oil:
22. stearyl alcohol:
23. glycol ester:
24. paradichlorobenzene:
25. euglenol:

26. ammonium alum:
27. benzoyl peroxide:
28. salicylic acid:
29. sucrose:
30. potassium chloride:
31. methyl paraben:
32. benzoic acid:
33. pectin:
34. ascorbic acid:
35. acetic acid:
36. ethyl acetate:
37. sodium tallowate:
39. citric acid:
40. sodium caseinate:
41. adipic acid:
42. fumaric acid:
43. glycerin:
44. lanolin:
45. isopropyl alcohol:
46. methanol:
47. ethylene glycol:
48. methanol:
49. bismuth sub-salicylate:
50. annatto:

21 For the Teacher

Objective

No trick here. In this activity, students will be challenged to take a closer look at common commercial products. Doing so will force students to be more observant and, hopefully, appreciative of the ordinary things around them we so often take for granted.

Materials Needed

None

Curiosity Hook

Bring in a few commercial products and set them where they can be viewed by the students.

Setup

1. Instruct students to take the list of chemicals shown on the student page to a supermarket.

2. Once there, students should read the labels of products and try to find those that contain the chemicals on their list.

3. Students should write the name of the product beside the chemical.

4. Allow students a fixed amount of time, say two or three days, to complete the task. Encourage students to involve parents, siblings, and friends in the quest.

5. Award one point for each product and chemical matched. Consider presenting a gag trophy/gift to the student with the highest point total. Have students share their findings. Hopefully, they will be able to complete the entire list.

Safety Concerns

Use common sense.

Application

Chemistry has changed our lives in many ways. In a class brainstorming session, have students think about chemistry connections and compile a list of products or ways in which chemistry has influenced and affected their lives.

22 Law of Lenz

Problem: *Will the magnet fall at the same rate through each type of tube?*

Observe

1. Observe and describe what happens as the teacher drops a nonmagnetic object down each tube. Record the time it takes the nonmagnetic object to fall the length of each tube.

   A. Plastic tube: **B.** Copper tube:

   C. Aluminum tube: **D.** Brass tube:

Predict

2. What will happen when the teacher drops a powerful magnet down each tube? Will the rate of fall be the same, faster, or slower in each tube?

Conclude

3. Record the rate of fall of the magnet in each tube. Was the rate of fall of the magnet the same in each tube? How would you explain any discrepancies you observed?

    A. Plastic tube: **B.** Copper tube:

    C. Aluminum tube: **D.** Brass tube:

22 For the Teacher

Objective

In this activity, students will be challenged to explain any discrepancies they observe as a powerful magnet falls down a series of tubes.

Background Information

In 1834, H. F. Lenz determined that the force on the wires of an armature opposes the original motion of the wires, slowing down the rotation of the armature. From this, he formulated Lenz's law which states the following: *The direction of the induced current is such that the magnetic field resulting from the induced current opposes the change in flux that caused the induced current.* How does this law relate to this activity? This law will help explain the discrepancies in the rate of fall of a powerful magnet through tubes of various materials.

Materials Needed

- 1 powerful magnet (What are called "cow magnets" will work, as will neodymium magnets. Powerful but inexpensive magnets can be purchased from most scientific supply companies. Local meat packing plants may be a source for cow magnets.)

- tubes of various materials (I suggest at least one tube each of plastic, copper, aluminum, and brass. Each tube should be the same length [about 3 feet] and just slightly larger in diameter than the magnet.)

- 1 piece of nonmagnetic material about the same size and shape as the magnet (a lump of plastic will work)

- cookie sheet or aluminum pie pan

Curiosity Hook

Do some manipulation with magnets as students enter the room.

Setup

1. Show students each type of tube. Point out that each tube is approximately the same length and diameter.

2. Demonstrate that the nonmagnetic object is not attracted to any of the tubes.

3. Drop the nonmagnetic object down each tube. Have students record how long it takes the nonmagnetic object to fall the length of each tube. Place a cookie sheet or aluminum pie pan under each tube before you drop the object. The sound of the object hitting the pan will tell you and the students when the object has fallen the length of the tube. Under 1 on the student page, have students record time of fall for each tube.

4. Now demonstrate that the magnet is also not attracted to any of the tubes.

5. Have students predict whether the magnet will fall at the same rate, faster, or slower than the nonmagnetic object. Have students record their predictions under 2 on the student page.

6. Drop the magnet down each tube and have students record the rate of fall in each tube under 3 on the student page.

Safety Concerns

Use common sense.

Outcomes and Explanations

As the magnet falls through the tube, the magnetic field around it is constantly changing. As Lenz's law would predict, *This changing magnetic field induces the flow of eddy currents through the metallic tubes only. These eddy currents have a magnetic field of their own which opposes the fall of the magnet, causing it to move more slowly down the metal tubes. Thus, the magnet should fall faster from the nonmetallic pipe or those metal pipes that are nonmagnetic.*

Application

Eddy currents are generated from transformers and often lead to power losses. This is prevented by using insulating glue between the thin strips of the transformer. Also many modern automobiles have an electronic ignition system that varies the magnetic field. An aluminum armature with 4, 6, or 8 protrusions (depending on the number of spark plugs) spins. Each protrusion, in turn, passes through the magnetic field, causing it to vary.

Challenge student to investigate this effect further in class (they almost certainly lack the necessary equipment to do this at home). Ask them, Does the thickness of the tube make a difference? Does the length make a difference? Will tubes made of other substances—steel, glass, etc.— show the same effect?

23 Pootsie Wootsie's Challenge

Problem: *Can you reverse the arrangement of balls in the bowls?*

Observe

1. In the space below, diagram and describe the system you see before you.

Predict

2. Your little cousin, Pootsie Wootsie, has a challenge for you. Change the arrangement of balls in the container so that you end up with the metal balls on top, the ping pong balls on the bottom, and the beans in-between. You may touch the container, but you may not put your hands in the container. In the space below, explain how you would meet this challenge.

Conclude

3. How did the teacher meet the challenge? Explain how the teacher's method works.

23 For the Teacher

Objective

In this activity, students will have to use critical thinking to meet Pootsie Wootsie's challenge.

Materials Needed

- 3 or 4 ping-pong balls

- 3 or 4 metal balls about the same size as the ping-pong balls (Steel ball bearings will work. You might get these free from a repair shop that works on heavy equipment.)

- large clear container such as a glass mixing bowl

- enough dry beans to cover the ping-pong balls in the bottom of the container

Curiosity Hook

If you have the talent for it, you could be juggling some of the balls as students enter the room. For most of us, it would probably be more practical to be bouncing a ping-pong ball off the floor and catching it as students enter the room.

Setup

1. Ahead of time, place the ping-pong balls in the bottom of the clear container, cover them with dry beans, and lay the metal balls on top of the beans.

2. Set the container where students can observe it. Have students write their description under 1 on the student page.

3. Now present Pootsie Wootsie's challenge to the students. Make sure they understand the rules as explained under 2 on the student page. Give students time to think about this silently, and then have them write their solution(s) to the challenge under 2 on the student page.

4. Students share their solutions with the rest of the class.

5. Now show the students your solution to the challenge. Gently shake the bowl. The ping-pong balls will rise to the top, the metal balls will sink to the bottom, and the beans will remain in-between. Have students write your solution under 3 on the student page.

Safety Concerns

Use common sense.

Outcomes and Explanations

The two types of balls and the beans all have different densities. The metal balls have the highest density, the ping-pong balls have the lowest density, and the beans have a density somewhere in-between. When you first start shaking the container, all the objects are free to move around. The metal balls, being the densest, "sink" and the ping-pong balls, being the least dense, "float" to the top. Have students write this explanation under 3 on the student page.

Application and Take Home

Challenge students to find examples of this effect at home. Dry packaged foods like potato chips and cereal will show this same kind of density layering due to shaking during shipment.

24 Alien Inverting Light

Problem: *What causes some words to invert but not others?*

Observe

1. Last night, the teacher was visited by aliens. As a reminder of their visit, they left a special bulb that produces a strange beam of light that inverts words. The teacher will now demonstrate this light to you. Unfortunately, our overhead projector has only half the power needed to fully energize the special bulb. As you observe and ponder, answer the following questions:

    A. What two words is the teacher going to use the special light on?

    B. What happened when the teacher used the special light on the two words?

Conclude

2. Explain what you just saw.

24 For the Teacher

Objective

As we continue to stress in this book, things are not always as they seem. In this activity, students will need to use their powers of careful observation and critical thinking to solve the problem of why one word inverts but the other doesn't.

Materials Needed

- 2 pieces of transparency film
- overhead projector and view screen (a light-colored wall will also work)
- spare overhead projector bulb

Curiosity Hook

Before class begins, place Transparency A on the overhead projector, but do not turn the overhead on. Have the room dark as students enter. Once they are all seated, turn on the overhead projector. The students should read

TITANIUM

DIOXIDE

on the screen. Now set the scene (see the material under 1 on the student page), and show them the special "alien" bulb. Have students record the words on Transparency A under 1A on the student sheet.

Setup

1. Ahead of time, prepare two transparencies as shown on the top right of this page. You can write the words on the transparency by hand or print them on paper first and use the printout to burn a transparency. However you do it, the letters need to be all caps, as dark as possible, and about 1" to 2" tall.

Transparency A

```
TITANIUM

DIOXIDE
```

Transparency B

```
DIOXIDE

TITANIUM
```

2. Once you have set the scene, turn the projector off. Now (still in dark), tell students you are going to put the special alien bulb into the overhead projector. Remove Transparency A, unplug the overhead projector (you don't want to electrocute yourself), and switch the bulbs or at least pretend to switch them. Now, place Transparency B on the overhead face down and flipped so that the bottom is now at the top:

Transparency B

```
ꓕꓶꓕ∀NIꓵM

DIOXIDE
```

Students must not notice that you switched Transparency A with Transparency B. I suggest you practice all this in the dark several times before you actually attempt this ruse in class.

3. Plug the overhead projector back in, and turn it on.

4. Students should observe that the word

TITANIUM appears inverted but the word DIOXIDE does not. Tell them you were afraid of this. Since the overhead projector had only half the power needed for the special bulb, only one word was inverted. Have the students record this observation under 1B on the student page.

Safety Concerns

Use common sense.

Outcomes and Explanations

Things are not always as they appear. Both words are actually inverted. However, the trick is that the word DIOXIDE (in all caps) looks the same right side up or upside down. Have students write this explanation under 2 on the student page.

Application

Use this activity as a lead. Take a few minutes to discuss the role of careful observation in science. Some background information on observing is given in the Introduction section of this book.

25 A Pint of Tension

Problem: *Will the water pour out of the jar through the screen?*

Observe

1. In the space below, diagram and describe the system you see before you.

Predict

2. Predict what will happen when the teacher inverts the jar of water and removes the card.

Conclude

3. What did happen when the jar of water was inverted? Why did it happen that way? Explain.

Predict

4. Can you figure out a way to get the water out? (No! You cannot remove the lid of the jar.)

Conclude

5. How did the teacher get the water out of the jar? How does the teacher's method work?

25 For the Teacher

Objective

This activity is a good example of what is called a "counterintuitive demonstration" in science jargon. That is, what happens is the opposite of what experience and logic dictate should happen. Experience and logic will tell students that the water should pour out the screen covering on the jar. However, it will not happen that way and students will be challenged to solve this apparent discrepancy.

Materials Needed

- 1-pint canning jar
- 1 container (to be used for Curiosity Hook)
- 1 threaded rim or ring to fit the pint canning jar
- a piece of fine mesh wire window screen slightly larger than the mouth of the jar
- hand soap dispenser
- 1 toothpick
- 1 3" x 5" note card

Curiosity Hook

Pour water back and forth from one container to another as students enter the classroom.

Setup

1. Ahead of time, cut the screen into a circular shape that fits into the threaded rim. Fill the jar with water, place the piece of screen inside the rim, and screw the rim onto the jar.

2. Have the jar of water with the rim and screen in place sitting where students can observe it. Have students write their descriptions and diagrams of this device under 1 on the student page.

3. Now place the note card on top of the jar of water and invert it, holding onto the card. Ask students to hypothesize what will happen when you remove the card. Students should write their predictions under 2 on the student page.

4. With the jar of water still inverted, remove the card. No water will come out of the jar. Take a toothpick and stick it up into the holes in the screen. Still no water will come out. Have students record this result under 3 on the student page.

5. Now challenge students to figure out a way to get the water out without removing the lid. Students should write their solution(s) to the problem under 4 on the student page. Put the card back on the jar, turn it right side up, and set it where students can see it as they ponder the problem.

6. Use the card and again invert the jar of water. Remove the card. Put a small amount of soap on your finger and rub it across the screen. The water will now rush out of the jar. Have students record this result under 5 on the student page.

Safety Concerns

Clean up any spills. Remember, soap and water can be slippery!

Outcomes and Explanations

1. Why doesn't the water rush out through the screen? The secret lies in the molecules of the water. Water molecules attract each other and tend to "stick" together (cohesion). When this happens at the surface of the water, the water molecules become tightly packed and a

"skin" forms on the surface. This thin layer ("skin") of tightly packed water molecules is called surface tension. The forces of surface tension of the water are greater than the weight of the water (gravitational pull) downward, so no water can leave the jar. Discuss this with students and have them write this explanation under 3 on the student page.

2. Soaps and detergents have the property of weakening the cohesive (attracting) forces between the water molecules. When you apply the soap to the screen, you destroy the surface tension of the water molecules and the weight of the water (gravitational pull) is great enough to cause water to rush out of the jar. Have students write this explanation under 5 on the student page.

Application

1. Students who have spent any time around the edge of a lake or pond may have seen small insects "walking on water" due to surface tension.

2. As demonstrated in this activity, soaps and detergents reduce the surface tension of water. This property makes them useful for washing clothes or hands. By reducing the surface tension, soaps and detergents make it easier to get the dirt out and off.

Take Home

Because of surface tension, even a steel needle, (if carefully positioned), can be made to float on water. Challenge students to investigate on their own the effects that weight and shape have on the ability of objects to float due to surface tension.

26 The Falling Argument (or Aristotle vs. Galileo)

Problem: *Aristotle argued that heavy objects fall faster than light objects. Later, Galileo would state that light and heavy objects fall at the same rate. Who was right? Could there be more to it than that?*

Predict

1. The teacher will drop two objects of different weights from the same height at the same time. Predict which one will hit the floor first.

Conclude

2. Which object did hit the floor first? Based on your observations, who was correct, Aristotle or Galileo?

Predict

3. The teacher will now drop two pieces of paper—one crumpled up into a ball, the other flat and unaltered—from the same height at the same time. Predict which piece of paper will hit the floor first.

Conclude

4. Which piece of paper did hit the floor first? From this observation, what can you say about Aristotle's and Galileo's statements? Explain.

26 For the Teacher

Objective

Scientific principles are often oversimplified or incompletely stated. The result is confusion. In this activity, students are challenged to find the qualifier in Galileo's law of falling bodies.

Materials Needed

- 2 objects of different weights (I suggest using pennies. Stack 3 or 4 pennies and tape them together. Use a single penny as the other [lighter] object.)

- 2 sheets of paper both the same size

- optional—a stepladder

Curiosity Hook

Roll a ping-pong ball or tennis ball off your hand. Let it bounce off the floor, and catch it as students enter the room.

Setup

1. Discuss the disagreement between Aristotle and Galileo as to the rate of fall of objects of different weights. See the material under the Problem heading on the student page.

2. Show students the single penny in one hand (or a light object) and the stack of taped pennies (or a heavy object) in the other hand. Have students predict which object will hit the floor first when both are dropped from the same height at the same time. Have students write their predictions under 1 on the student page.

3. Now drop both objects at the same time from the same height. The results will be easier to discern if you get higher, say on a chair, a desk, or even a ladder. Both

objects should hit the floor at approximately the same time.

4. Have students record the result under 2 on the student page.

5. Now show the students two sheets of paper, both the same size. Crumple one sheet but do nothing to the other sheet. Ask students to predict which will hit the floor first when both are dropped at the same time from the same height. Have students record their predictions under 3 on the student page.

6. Drop both sheets of paper from the same height at the same time. The crumpled paper should hit the floor first.

Safety Concerns

Use caution if you get up on a chair, ladder, or table to drop the objects. Remember—it's not the fall that hurts, it's the sudden stop.

Outcomes and Explanations

1. Galileo was correct. Objects of different weights fall at the same rate. Students should record this under 2 on the student page.

2. However, when two pieces of paper of the same weight are dropped, they both don't hit the floor at the same time. Is Galileo correct only some of the time? Is gravity not constant? The discrepancy here is the shape of the paper. The flat, unaltered sheet has greater air resistance than the crumpled sheet of paper so it falls more slowly. The qualifier is air resistance. Thus, Galileo's law of falling objects should be stated: Assuming no air resistance, all objects fall to Earth with a constant acceleration. Have students

write this explanation under 4 on the student page.

Application

Actually, Galileo's law of falling objects is only totally correct in a vacuum where there is no air resistance at all. This was eloquently proven by Apollo astronauts who dropped a geologist's pick and a feather and relayed back that they both hit the surface of the airless moon at the same time.

Take Home

What is the relationship between size, shape, and weight and the rate of fall of various objects? For what objects can air resistance be ignored? For what objects can air resistance not be ignored? Encourage students to investigate further on their own. The next Galileo may be sitting in your class right now just waiting for you to fan his/her inner fire into a flame.

27 Playing Catchup

Problem: *Will the top ball catch the lower ball?*

Observe

1. In the space below, diagram and describe the system you see before you.

Predict

2. If the teacher releases both balls from different positions at the same time, will they get closer together, farther apart, or maintain their original distance as they roll down the ramp?

Conclude

3. What did happen when both balls were released at the same time?

Predict

4. What will happen when the teacher releases one ball from the top and then releases the second ball when the first ball reaches the 8-inch mark? Will the balls get closer together, farther apart, or maintain their original distance?

Conclude

5. What did happen when the balls were released at different times? Why did it happen that way?

27 For the Teacher

Objective

In this activity, students will be challenged to discern the difference between acceleration and velocity.

Materials Needed

- 1 V-shaped ramp about 3' to 4' long (Two meter sticks taped together will work. You could also tape, nail, or glue together two pieces of scrap wood from your industrial technology department. The metal channel used over outside corners when hanging sheet rock is an excellent ramp as well.)

- 2 balls (Steel ball bearings or large marbles will work nicely.)

Curiosity Hook

Roll one of the balls down the ramp as students enter the classroom.

Setup

1. Set the ramp up ahead of time. Place one or two textbooks under one end of the ramp so that the ramp is inclined. Do not make the ramp too high or the balls will roll so fast that the students will have difficulty seeing the results. The high end of the ramp will be considered the top. Tape the ramp to the books to assure stability.

2. Place three black marks or pieces of tape on the ramp—one mark about 8 inches from the top (which we will refer to as Position 1), another about 16 inches from the top, and a third about 24 inches from the top. These marks will help students gauge the distance between the balls as they roll down the ramp. Have students

diagram and describe the system under 1 on the student page.

3. Place and hold one ball at the top of the ramp and one ball at Position 1. Tell students you are going to release both balls at the same time. Have students predict whether the balls will get closer together, farther apart, or maintain their original distance as they roll down the ramp. Students should write their predictions under 2 on the student page.

4. Release the balls. Have students record the results under 3 on the student page. You will want to repeat this several times to insure consistent results.

5. Now place and hold one ball at the top of the ramp. Tell students you are going to release the ball. When it gets to Position 1, you are going to release the second ball from the top of the ramp. Have students predict whether the balls will get closer together, farther apart, or maintain their original distance as they roll down the ramp. Have students write their predictions under 4 on the student page.

6. Release the balls. Have students record the results under 5 on the student page.

Safety Concerns

Use common sense.

Outcomes and Explanations

1. In both setups, some students will predict that the top ball will gain on the bottom ball. These students are confusing speed with velocity and/or confusing velocity with acceleration.

2. Speed can be defined as how fast some-

thing is moving (rate of motion) while velocity can be thought of as the rate of motion (speed) in a specific direction. Velocity then describes both speed and direction. Acceleration, on the other hand, can be defined as the rate of change in velocity. Both balls gain the same amount of velocity each time, so both balls have the same acceleration on the ramp. There is no way one ball can gain on the other, so they maintain their original distance from each other down the ramp.

3. Discuss speed, velocity, and acceleration with students and have them write this explanation under 5 on the student page.

Application

Use these problems to reinforce student understanding of speed, velocity, and acceleration:

1. You turn on the radio and hear just the end of a news story about killer bees. The swarm, moving at a speed of 10 miles per hour, has just left a town 5 miles north of your location. What should you do? (Unfortunately, you don't have enough information to make a decision.

You know the speed of the swarm but not the direction [velocity]).

2. What velocity of the swarm should make you nervous? (10 miles per hour [speed] south [direction].)

3. How could you turn the speedometer of your car into a velocity meter? (Attach a compass to the dashboard so that speed and direction could be read simultaneously.)

4. Describe three different ways to change your velocity while riding a bicycle. (Pedal faster, apply the brakes, and change directions.)

5. Have volunteers demonstrate two different walking velocities in the same direction, two different walking velocities with the same speed, and an acceleration walk.

Take Home

Encourage students to take home what they have learned and teach their parents, siblings, and friends the true nature of speed, velocity, and acceleration.

28 The Boiling Discrepancy

Problem: *Can you explain the boiling discrepancy?*

Observe

1. In the space below, diagram and describe the system you see before you.

Predict

2. Predict the temperature in

Beaker A _____

Beaker B _____

Conclude

3. Was there a discrepancy (difference) in the temperatures between the two beakers? If there was a discrepancy, list all the explanations you can think of.

28 For the Teacher

Objective

In this activity, students will be challenged to explain the discrepancy in temperature between two seemingly identical systems.

Materials Needed

- 2 hot plates (If you have gas outlets handy and have ring stands, Bunsen burners will also work. In fact, if you want to save time heating the water, Bunsen burners will do it faster than hot plates.)

- 2 beakers of the same size (Exact size is not important but the larger the beaker, the longer it will take to heat the water to boiling. I use 600-ml beakers with about 400 ml to 450 ml of water in each.)

- distilled water (You will need enough to fill each beaker about half full. Tap water often contains minerals which will influence the outcome of the demonstration.)

- small amount of table salt

- 2 chemical thermometers

Curiosity Hook

To save time, have the systems set up, the heat turned on, and be stirring each beaker with a thermometer as students enter the classroom.

Setup

1. Ahead of time, put both hot plates where students can see them. Fill both beakers with equal amounts of distilled water.

2. In one beaker (System A), add only the distilled water. In the other beaker (System B), add a small amount of salt— about 20 to 30 grams (pinches) should do it (1 pinch = approx. 1 gram). Add a

few pinches and then stir. You do not want the water to become cloudy with salt or the excess, undissolved salt to settle onto the bottom of the beaker. Both beakers should look like they have only water in them. This is what students should see as they come in:

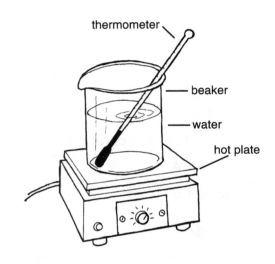

System A

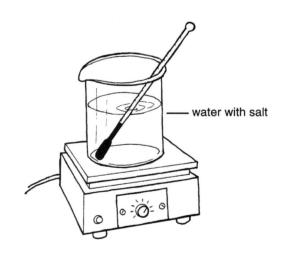

System B

3. Both systems should appear identical in all apparent aspects to students. Have students observe the systems and record

their diagrams and descriptions under 1 on the student page.

4. As the beakers are heating, have students discuss the process of boiling. Ask them to explain how they know when something is boiling. (Visually—bubbles form and burst, steam rises. Physically—a temperature of 212° F or 100° C or the temperature at which the water begins to evaporate.)

5. Once the water has reached an obvious boil in System A, have students predict what the temperature is in both systems. Students should record their predictions under 2 on the student page.

6. Now read out loud the temperature on both thermometers. The temperature on the thermometer in System B should be higher than the one in System A. However, System B should show no or few signs of boiling compared to System A. 20 grams of salt will raise the boiling point of water about 2° C and 30 grams of salt will raise it about 4° C.

7. Have students hypothesize possible explanations to explain this discrepancy. List the various hypotheses on the board where students can see and react to them.

Safety Concerns

You should wear safety goggles when working around hot liquids. Position students where they can safely see but not be in danger if boiling water should spill.

Outcomes and Explanations

The salt added to System B elevates (increases) its boiling temperature. The molecules of salt form what are called solute par-

ticles between the molecules of water. These solute particles interfere with the evaporation of water. Thus, more energy is needed to allow the water molecules to evaporate and the solution boils at a higher temperature.

Discuss this with students, and have them write this explanation under 3 on the student page.

Application

1. Share the graph below with students, and have them predict if adding more salt would cause the graph to continue in the same pattern or level off. (The graph would continue until saturation was reached and then level off because no more salt could dissolve.)

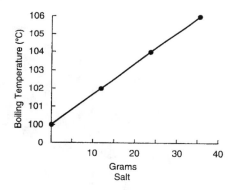

2. Have students discuss where we use this knowledge of boiling point elevation in practical ways in our daily life. (Antifreeze raises the boiling point of water in a car radiator. As a result, the radiator does a more efficient job of removing damaging heat from the engine.)

3. Challenge students to investigate further. Would using different stuff (solute particles) give different results? Will sugar work or maybe coffee creamer?

29 Strange Marks

Problem: *Things are not always as they appear. What is the reality of this situation?*

Observe

1. Carefully observe the diagram, and write as many accurate observations as you can within the time limit set by the teacher.

   My accurate observations of the diagram are as follow:

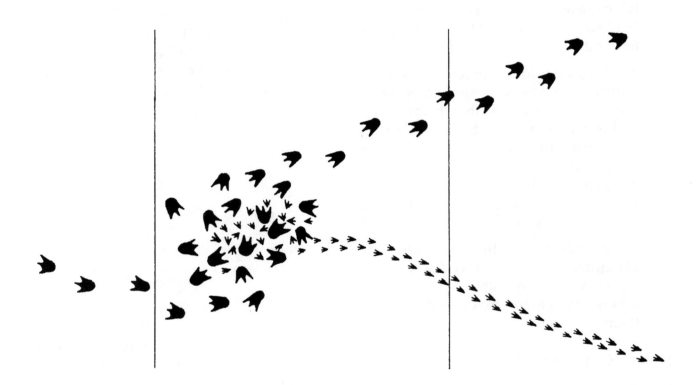

Conclude

2. Were all your observations accurate? What is the difference between an observation and an inference?

29 For the Teacher

Objective

There is no trick or discrepant event in this activity. Instead, students will be challenged to distinguish between observation and inference.

Materials Needed

None

Curiosity Hook and Setup

1. Use what I call the "Bright Yellow Bird" example to lead into this activity. Once students are settled into their seats, select a student volunteer. Have the volunteer close his/her eyes or put his/her head down. Now write the following sentence in large letters on the chalkboard or a large piece of paper:

   > "The bright yellow bird
   > sat and sang his
   > heart out in the
   > the tall, green tree."

   Helpful hints:

   A. Make sure the student volunteer cannot see the sentence as you write it.

   B. There is not a misprint in the sentence. There should be two "the's" in the sentence but one "the" must end the first line and the second "the" must start the second line.

2. Instruct the student volunteer (eyes still closed or head still down) to read the sentence immediately as he/she sees it, in a nice, loud voice. (The volunteer should not read the sentence silently first and then aloud to the rest of the class.)

3. Most students will never see or read the second "the." I have had student volunteers read this five or six times with their voices growing louder with frustration each time I tell them to read it again. They never see the second "the" until I point it out to them. In fact, many students in the rest of the class who watched you write the sentence on the board in the first place will not see the second "the."

4. Make the point that there is a difference between what you think you see or want to see (inference) and what is really there (accurate observation).

5. Now have students turn their attention to the strange marks in the diagram under 1 on the student page. Instruct them to write as many accurate observations as possible within a time limit of, say, five minutes.

6. Once the time limit is up, have students share some of their observations. Write these on the board or a large sheet of paper. Have students vote on which descriptions on the list are accurate observations and which are inferences.

Safety Concerns

Use common sense.

Outcomes and Explanations

Most of what passes for observation in our daily lives is actually inference. Any observation is the unique perspective of the observer, colored and altered by his/her experiences, emotions, and especially preconceived expectations. Very few people ever see the second "the" in the Bright Yellow Bird example. Why? They don't expect it to be there.

What is the reality of the diagram on the student page? There are two vertical parallel lines (you will be surprised at the number of students who don't see these lines) and a series of dark marks of various sizes. When describing the diagram, most students will list only inferences. Some will see dinosaur prints (The big dinosaur and little dinosaur struggle and the big dinosaur eats the little one.), birds, fish, and other things that aren't actually there. Discuss the difference between observation (what is there) and inference (what we think is there), and have students write these definitions under 2 on the student page.

Take Home

Encourage students to take the diagram as well as the Bright Yellow Bird example with them, and use them to teach their parents, siblings, and friends the difference between observation and inference.

30 Weightless Water

Problem: *What will the water do as the cup falls?*

Observe

1. In the space below, diagram and describe the system the teacher is preparing.

Predict

2. Predict what will happen to the water in the cup when the cup is dropped.

Conclude

3. How did the water in the cup behave when the cup was dropped, and why did it happen that way?

30 For the Teacher

Objective

In this activity, students will grapple with the concept of weight vs. weightlessness and attempt to understand why astronauts and satellites only appear to be weightless.

Materials Needed

- 1 large Styrofoam cup (The size of the cup is not critical.)

- sharpened pencil

- enough colored water to fill the cup about 2/3 full (Color the water with ordinary food coloring.)

- bathroom scale

- optional—a stepladder

Curiosity Hook

Stand on the scale as students enter the room. If you are sensitive about your weight, ask one of the first students who enters to stand on the scale in your place.

Setup

1. Open the lesson by posing the following questions to students:

   A. What is weight? Define it. (Weight can be defined as the measure of the force of gravity on an object. That is, the gravity of the earth pulls everything toward it. This pull of gravity is what we know as weight.)

   B. How does the scale measure your weight? (There is a spring inside the scale so that when you step on the scale, the downward force of gravity—your weight—is balanced by the upward force exerted by the spring. The dial on the scale, which

is marked off in units of weight, moves as the spring stretches. When the spring stops moving, the number shown on the dial indicates your weight.)

2. Now take the pencil and poke two smooth, clean holes in the cup—one in the bottom and one in the side. Pour some water into the cup and let it flow out the holes. Ask students why water flows out the holes. (The water has weight. That is, gravity pulls the water down through the holes.)

3. Now put your fingers over the holes and fill the cup with colored water. Have students describe and diagram this system under 1 on the student page.

4. Ask students to predict what will happen to the water in the cup if you drop the cup. Have students write their predictions under 2 on the student page.

5. Drop the cup and have students observe how the water behaves. Dropping the cup from a higher point, say off the top of a stepladder, will give students a longer opportunity to note that the water stays in the cup and does not flow out as the cup falls.

Safety Concerns

Water will fly everywhere when you drop the cup, so you might consider conducting this activity outside.

Outcomes and Explanations

Why doesn't the water flow out of the holes as the cup is dropped? Has the water suddenly become weightless? No, the water and the cup both still have weight. As they fall, gravity is pulling on them both equally. When you held the cup, water flowed out the holes because you prevented the cup, but not the water, from being pulled toward the earth.

Ask students to ponder this question: If you were standing on the scale in an elevator and the elevator suddenly dropped, what would the reading on the scale be? (If you were falling fast enough [9.80 meter/second^2], the scale would read zero. As with the falling cup of water, gravity would be pulling on you and the scale equally. Hence, you would appear to have no weight.) Discuss this with students and have them write the explanation under 3 on the student page.

Application

We see astronauts floating around in spacecraft and space stations all the time. Are they really weightless? No, this is another example of things not being as they appear. In orbit, the astronauts and their space craft are both falling. They don't fall downward because the speed of the spaceship outward matches the downward pull of gravity. So the astronauts and their craft are free-falling around the earth rather than toward it. As with the cup of water and the scales in the elevator, gravity is pulling on the astronauts and their ship equally so they seem to be weightless in relation to each other.

Take Home

This activity can be easily and safely done by students outside the classroom. Encourage students to demonstrate this phenomenon to their parents, siblings, and/or friends in order to teach them the difference between weight and apparent weightlessness. They will spill water, so caution them to conduct their demonstration in a location where spills can be easily contained or cleaned.

31 The Dilemma of Ignaz Semmelweis

Problem: *What is causing the mysterious deaths in the maternity ward?*

Imagine

Imagine the following scenario: You are Ignaz Semmelweis, the young chief obstetrician of one of the finest teaching hospitals of its time in Vienna, Austria, in 1843. Each day, at least one out of every six women in your maternity ward becomes sick with what is called "childbed fever" (puerperal fever) and will probably die within a short time. This will continue unless you make a startling connection and implement an unusual experiment. You have the following facts in hand: The hospital wards include surgery, traumatic accidents, maternity, intensive care, psychiatric care, and infectious disease. When maternity and other patients die, their bodies are placed in the autopsy room of the morgue in preparation for the following day's teaching lesson. In the morning, doctors and medical students register individually for class and then proceed to the autopsy room. Autopsies are done to determine the probable cause of death of each person. The doctors and students leave the morgue as a group. After they change their soiled lab coats for clean ones, they start the day's examination tour with the maternity ward. They perform thorough pelvic examinations on some of the women in the maternity ward. They change their lab coats again and then move on to the ward for traumatic accident patients. Each day, students and doctors make rounds through the entire hospital. During one day, 11 out of 12 of your maternity patients suddenly begin to run high fevers. That night, more of your patients become so sick that they must be removed from the ward. By the third night, most of the affected patients are dead; their bodies have been wheeled to the autopsy room for the next day's lesson. You are depressed and tired. Suddenly an insight hits you with the force of lightning!

Predict

1. What connection did Ignaz Semmelweis make? What did he think was spreading this mysterious fever mainly to women in the maternity ward?

Design

2. Design an experiment to test your prediction.

31 For the Teacher

Objective

Using a historical example, students will be challenged in this activity to make a lifesaving connection and to design an experiment to test the validity of their insight.

Materials Needed

- surgical mask (to be used in Curiosity Hook)

Curiosity Hook

Wear a surgical mask as students enter the classroom.

Safety Concerns

None

Outcomes and Explanations

Sometimes a hypothesis is made before there is enough information to support it. Such is the case with Ignaz Semmelweis. Some 40 years before microorganisms were found to cause disease, Semmelweis postulated that doctors carried the disease-causing agent that caused puerperal fever ("childbed fever") on their hands. Because doctors began the day's examination tour with the maternity ward, they spread the agent mainly to women in the maternity ward. Hopefully, students will make this connection under 1 on the student page. (Have them write their answer.)

Semmelweis tested his idea experimentally by having one group of doctors wash their hands before examining women in the maternity ward. (This would have been the experimental group.) Another group of doctors maintained their usual routine and did not wash their hands before examining the women. (This would have been the control group.) The dilemma Semmelweis faced was that if he was correct, he was dooming some women (the control group) to nearly certain death. Discuss this with students, and have them write their experimental designs under 2 on the student page.

Semmelweis was correct. When doctors washed their hands before examining women and delivering babies, the number of women who developed the fever dropped dramatically, and many lives were saved. Today, Semmelweis's conclusion may seem obvious, but the doctors of his day resisted it. With no theory to explain how dirty hands could cause fever, most doctors refused to even consider washing their hands.

Fortunately, today, childbed fever is virtually unheard of; when it does occur, it is easily treated with antibiotics. Ironically, Semmelweis died of the very disease he fought so hard to bring under control. His death was the result of contracting the fever after accidentally cutting himself during a dissection procedure in the morgue.

32 The Ransom for Renard

Problem: *Which pen was used to write the ransom note?*

Background Information

1. Imagine the following scenario:

   Mrs. Prixie DePoo, wife of the late and very rich industrialist, Philpot DePoo, loves her little dog, Renard, more than anything, but Renard is missing. She and all her servants have searched her mansion and grounds high and low, but Renard is nowhere to be found. Has Renard been dognapped? The police believe so, and their suspicions are confirmed when Mrs. De Poo receives a ransom note demanding a huge sum of money in exchange for the safe return of Renard. The police quickly arrest three suspects and then turn to you, Dr. Bumpy Buckmeister, famous forensic scientist, to solve the case.

Predict

2. You have the following facts to work with:

   A. The ransom note was written on a paper towel.

   B. The ransom note was written with a black felt-tipped pen.

   C. Each of the suspects had a black felt-tipped pen in their pocket when they were brought in.

   D. The ink in each pen is water-soluble.

Design

3. The pen used to write the note must belong to the dognapper. Design a way of determining which suspect's pen wrote the ransom note. In the space below, describe how you would solve this problem.

Conclude

4. Which suspect wrote the ransom note? How can you tell?

32 For the Teacher

Objective

In this activity, students will play the role of a forensic scientist and use chromatography to determine which pen was used to write the ransom for Renard.

Background Information

You may not realize it, but black ink is actually a mixture of several different colors. If you write your name on a paper towel with a black felt-tipped pen and then dip the towel in water, the black ink will separate into a band of different colors when the water reaches it. This is a simple example of ink chromatography. The colored pattern that forms on the paper towel is called a chromatograph. The inks in modern pens are made of a mixture of dyes. Since each company uses a slightly different ink formula, each brand of pen tends to have a unique chromatograph.

Materials Needed

- 3 black felt-tipped pens (Each pen should be manufactured by a different company and should contain water-soluble ink. You need to test the pens ahead of time to (1) make sure each pen does have water-soluble ink and (2) each pen does produce a unique chromatograph.)

- several pieces of paper towel (The more absorbent the towels, the better.)

- beaker (The 500 ml size should work nicely.)

- flat pan (A large glass or metal cake pan will work.)

- enough water to fill the beaker and the pan about 1/4 full

- piece of wire long enough to fit across the top of the beaker

- scissors to cut strips of paper towel

- single-hole paper punch

- piece of cardboard slightly larger than one sheet of paper towel

Curiosity Hook

Pet a stuffed toy dog as students enter the classroom.

Setup

1. Ahead of time:

   A. Use one of the labeled pens to write a ransom note on a piece of paper towel. (Be creative and have some fun with this.)

   B. Put a loop of tape around each pen and on the tape mark—Pen #1 (Suspect #1), Pen #2 (Suspect #2), and Pen #3 (Suspect #3).

   C. Cut three strips from a piece of paper towel, and use the paper punch to make a hole in the square (top) end of each piece. Label each strip with a number.

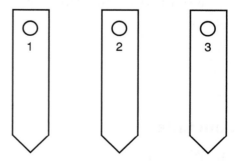

   D.
   Place the beaker, water, wire, numbered strips of towel, piece of cardboard, and pan close by—but out of sight to the students.

2. Begin by reading the scenario (under 1

on the student page) to students or have the students read the scenario silently to themselves. Show and read the ransom note to your students. Show the pens, and present the facts they have to work with (under 2 on the student page). Then challenge students to devise a way to determine which pen was used to write the ransom for Renard.

3. Have students brainstorm ways of solving this problem. Through leading questions and carefully placed hints, lead them, if necessary, to the plan of using chromatography to test the inks in each pen. For example, "Is there a way to determine any differences in the pens used?" Have students write their plans for solving the problem under 3 on the student page.

4. Now fill the large pan about 1/4 full of water, and hold the ransom note so that one edge is in the water. Do not put the entire note in the water or the ink will dissolve out into the water. The water will begin to creep up the towel and the black ink will begin to separate into colors (a chromatograph). You do not need to wait for the water to move up the entire towel. When a few lines of writing have begun to separate into color bands, lay the partially wet ransom note out onto the piece of cardboard. Pass this around so students can see the chromatograph formed by the ink on the ransom note.

5. Take each pen, and use it to make a large dot on the pointy end of each strip. Use pen #1 to make a dot on strip #1 and so on.

6. Place the wire through the holes at the

top of each strip. Place a small amount of water in the beaker, and hang the wire across the top of the beaker so that the

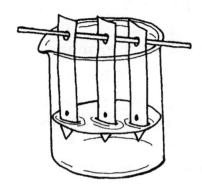

end of each towel strip just touches the water. The dot on each towel should not be down into the water or the ink will dissolve out into the water and not move up the towel.

Safety Concerns

Use common sense.

Outcomes and Explanations

Once chromatographs have formed on each strip, remove the strips and place them on the ransom note next to some of the letters on the note which have separated into chromatographs. Pass this around, and let students compare the chromatographs. Have students write their conclusion under 4 on the student page.

Application

The word chromatography means "color writing." Paper chromatography is an old tried-and-true method of separating parts of a mixture and is useful in forensics, food sciences, and biochemical and geological analysis.

33 The Problem of Grierer and Schramm

Problem: *What conclusions can you draw from the data on viruses?*

Background Information

1. Imagine the following scenario:

    You are Alfred Grierer, a biochemist. With your research partner, Gerhard Schramm, you are investigating a virus called the tobacco mosaic virus (TMV). This virus causes disease in certain types of plants.

2. You have the following facts:

    A. When fluids containing the virus are transferred from sick plants to healthy ones, the healthy plants come down with the disease.

    B. A virus is a tiny nonliving particle composed of a small strand of DNA or RNA (genes) covered by a coat of protein.

3. You do the following experiment:

    A. You centrifuge (spin at high speeds) a suspension of tobacco mosaic virus. This shatters the virus particles and separates the RNA (genes) from the protein coat.

    B. You inoculate some healthy plants with the separated viral RNA (Group I in the data table) and other healthy plants you inoculate with only the protein coats (Group II in the table).

4. Your results are shown in the following data table:

Group	I	II
Contains	RNA (+) — Protein (0)	RNA (0) — Protein (+)
Percent	RNA 99.98 — Protein 0.02	RNA 0 — Protein 100
Result	TMV infection	No TMV infection

Conclude

5. Is tobacco mosaic disease caused by the RNA (genes) of the virus or by the protein coat of the virus? Defend your answer.

33 For the Teacher

Objective

In this activity, students will use actual historical data and attempt to draw reasonable conclusions from this data.

Materials Needed

None

Curiosity Hook

Have a model, poster, or drawing of a virus where students can see it as they enter the classroom.

Setup

1. Read the scenario under 1 on the student page to your students, or have them read it silently to themselves.

2. Review the facts the students have to work with (under 2 on the student page).

3. Discuss the experiment performed by Grierer and Schramm as discussed on the student page. In this situation, each group was an experimental group, but each group then also served as a control (comparison) to the other group.

Safety Concerns

None

Outcomes and Explanations

The data table clearly shows that the RNA (genes) of the virus, not the protein coat, is responsible for causing tobacco mosaic disease in certain types of plants.

Application

Once virologists discovered the basic structure of viruses, they were at a loss to explain what part of the virus was responsible for the infectious nature of the virus.

Enter scientists Grierer and Schramm and their classic experiment detailed on the student page. Their important discovery greatly advanced our understanding of viruses and has been invaluable in controlling and preventing the diseases viruses cause.

34 "That's My Story, and I'm Sticking To It."

Problem: *What just happened?*

Observe and Describe

1. In the space below, accurately describe the situation that unfolded before you. You must complete your description within the time limit set by the teacher.

34 For the Teacher

Objective

In this activity, your students' powers of observation, perception, and recall will be challenged.

Materials Needed

None

Curiosity Hook

Do nothing out of the ordinary as students enter the room. The situation you present and ask them to describe should be unexpected.

Setup

1. Concoct a situation that you can spring unexpectedly on your students. Use your creativity and have fun with this. I cannot give a specific scenario that will work for everyone in all situations, but I would offer these suggestions:

    A. Try to use participants that your students are not familiar with. It may be easy for them to describe your fellow teacher across the hall or the principal, but more challenging to describe a total stranger(s).

    B. Keep it light. Given the social climate in schools today, it would be advisable to avoid scenes of violence.

    C. Keep it short. It is much more challenging if you spring this on students, and then have it end before they know what hit them.

    D. Put some strange twists of action and/or dialogue in your little play. Such unexpected "left turns" will test your students' ability to follow the reality of the situation.

Safety Concerns

Use common sense.

Outcomes and Explanation

1. Once your staged scenario has played out, challenge your students to accurately describe, under 1 on the student page, what just happened. You should instruct them to describe what the participants looked like, exactly what was said, and any actions or movements that occurred.

2. Make the challenge more difficult by giving your students only a short amount of time to record their observations. Three to five minutes is a reasonable time limit.

3. As time permits, have students share their descriptions, and then have the rest of the class critique them for accuracy. Accurate observation and description are the cornerstone of the scientific process and seem deceptively easy. You and your students will be amazed at how differently each student perceives the reality of what happened.

Application

As law enforcement officers can tell you and as recent studies have shown, eyewitness accounts of events, especially those in which the witness is afraid or highly excited, are fraught with inaccuracies. This would seem to be contradictory, but it is true. Why should people not be able to accurately describe what their own eyes have shown them? Any observation is the unique perspective of the observer and as such is colored and altered by the expectations, experiences, and prejudices of that observer. Add strong emotions, and inference (what people think they are seeing) replaces reality.

Take Home

Encourage students to make up their own scenarios and test the powers of accurate observation and description outside of class.

35 Backwards Boiling

Problem: *Do you really understand all you think you know about boiling?*

Observe

1. The teacher is going to boil water in an open flask. How will you know when the water is boiling? Give two indicators of boiling:

   A.

   B.

Predict

2. If the teacher removes the heat from the flask, will the water stop boiling? Why?

3. Will sealing the flask make any difference? The teacher will now use a rubber stopper with a thermometer in it (the thermometer will allow you to monitor the temperature of the water) to seal a flask of boiling water. Will the water stop boiling? Predict what will happen.

Conclude

4. What did happen, and why? Obviously, there must be something more to boiling than adding heat. What other factor is involved?

35 For the Teacher

Objective

In this activity, students will use their powers of observation, prediction, and critical thinking to investigate the less-than-obvious facets of the process of boiling.

Materials

- 1 round or flat-bottom flask (Size doesn't matter but the larger the flask, the easier it will be for students to see the results.)

- source of heat (If you have access to natural gas outlets, use a Bunsen burner. Otherwise, a butane burner or a hot plate will suffice. In a pinch, an alcohol burner will work. However, it will take a long time to boil water using only an alcohol burner.)

- 1 stand with ring and wire screen

- 1 one-hole rubber stopper that fits in the flask

- 2 chemical thermometers

- enough water to fill the flask nearly full

- container of ice cubes or crushed ice

- food coloring (This is optional and may be added to the water in the flask for visual effect.)

- safety goggles

- kitchen hot pads, heat resistant gloves or some other device for handling the flask of boiling water

Curiosity Hook

Have the flask of colored water set up and boiling where students can see it when they come into the classroom.

Setup

1. Ahead of time, insert one of the thermometers into the one-hole stopper. Use caution when doing this as the thermometer can break, possibly causing a puncture wound. Lubricate both the thermometer and stopper with water, and slowly twist the thermometer into the stopper. Your chemistry department may have a special device for safely inserting thermometers or tubing into stoppers. Once the stopper is inserted into the flask, the thermometer should reach down into the water or about 1/2 way down into the bulb of the flask.

2. Fill the flask about 3/4 full of water. The exact amount of water in the flask is not critical. Food coloring may be added to the water for visual effect.

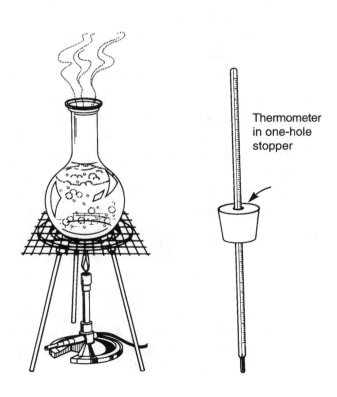

Thermometer in one-hole stopper

3. Add heat and begin boiling the water.

4. Question students about the process of boiling and the signs that show a liquid is in fact boiling. Have students answer question 1 on the student page.

5. Once the water in the flask is boiling vigorously, have students note the bubbling action of the water. Use the thermometer not inserted into the stopper to check the temperature of the water. The water should be near or at the boiling point.

6. Have students predict what will happen when the flame is removed from the flask. Have students write their predictions under 2 on the student page.

7. Now remove the flame from the flask. Have students note that the bubbling stops and use the thermometer to show that the temperature begins to fall.

8. Replace the flame under the flask so that the water boils again. Now ask students to predict what will happen if the flask of boiling water is sealed with the one-hole stopper containing a thermometer. Have students write their predictions under 3 on the student page.

9. Remove the flame from the flask and quickly insert the stopper-thermometer combination firmly into the flask. The flask must be sealed airtight for this demonstration to work. Use caution as the flask will be boiling hot and the steam rising out of the flask can cause burns.

10. To speed things up, lay the sealed flask on its side in a container of ice. Slowly rotate the flask every so often. The thermometer will show the temperature of the water falling but, amazingly, the water will continue to bubble (boil). I have cooled a sealed flask to as low as 25° C and still had bubbling (boiling).

Safety Concerns

1. You should wear safety goggles while conducting this demonstration.

2. Position students a safe distance from the heat source and boiling water.

3. Have some type of heat resistant materials ready—kitchen hot pads, special gloves, etc. for handling a boiling hot flask.

Outcomes and Explanations

1. When answering question #1 on the student page, students usually come up with two main signs of boiling:

   A. Bubbling

   B. Temperature. For your reference, the boiling point of water at sea level is 212° F or 100° C.

2. When the flame is removed from the boiling unsealed flask, the temperature drops and boiling stops. Obviously, heat is a major factor in boiling.

3. However, pressure also plays a role in boiling point. As the unsealed flask boils, steam is generated. This steam streams out the mouth of the flask, carrying some of the air in the flask with it. When the flask is then sealed, the air pressure inside the flask is considerably lower than the air pressure outside the flask.

4. Once students understand that the air pressure inside the flask is lower than the air pressure outside the flask, they should see a direct relationship between pressure and boiling point. The lower the air pressure, the lower the boiling point. Even though the temperature in the sealed flask falls well below the boiling point, the water obviously continues to boil (bubble). Discuss this with students, and have them write the explanation under 4 on the student page.

Application

1. Have students consider the following:

    A. Would water boil at a higher or lower temperature than normal on top of a mountain? (Normal indicates the boiling point at normal pressure, which is 760 mm of mercury or the barometric pressure at sea level.) Lower, because of the lower air pressure at that altitude. This is why many packaged foods have high altitude cooking instructions on the side of the package.

    B. Would water boil at a higher or lower temperature than normal in Death Valley? (Higher, because Death Valley is below sea level, and the air pressure would be greater, although it would take a very sensitive thermometer to detect the difference.)

Take Home

The safety hazard presented by flames and boiling hot water and the necessity of having specialized equipment make it impractical for students to duplicate this demonstration outside the classroom.

36 Off the Wall

Problem: *Can you attach a candle to a wall?*

Observe

1. In the space below, list the materials you see before you. The challenge is to attach the candle to a wall using only these construction supplies.

Design/Experiment

2. Think about the challenge, and come up with as many solutions to the problem as possible within the time limit set by the teacher.

36 For the Teacher

Objective

Inventors and scientists are creative, observant people who see connections, patterns, and solutions that others often overlook. This activity challenges students to "think vertically" and problem solve in something other than the customary horizontal dimension.

Materials Needed

- 1 candle
- 2 thumbtacks
- 1 box of wooden matches
- 1 piece of string 12 inches long

Curiosity Hook

Throw a candle against the wall as students enter the classroom. Tell the students that you are trying to attach the candle to the wall.

Setup

1. Using the Curiosity Hook as a lead, present the following challenge to your students:

   Have students observe the materials they have to work with. They should list these materials under 1 on the student page. Make sure they understand that these are the only materials that can be used to solve the problem but that not all of the materials have to be used. At this point, you also need to set a realistic minimum time that the candle must remain attached to the wall in order to qualify as a solution to the problem. The longer the attachment time you set, the more difficult the challenge. One minute (60 seconds) should be a realistic minimum attachment time.

2. Now have students brainstorm possible solutions to the problem using only the construction materials shown. Have them write their solutions under 2 on the student page. Complicate the problem by setting a time limit of 10 or 15 minutes on solution generation.

3. Once students have had time to generate solutions, have them share their solutions with the rest of the class.

Safety Concerns

Use common sense.

Outcomes and Explanations

As you can see, there are very few rules or guidelines for this challenge. Hopefully, free of constraint, students will let their creativity soar, and ingenious solutions will result. Encourage students to keep their designs as simple as possible. Charles Kettering said it best: "Invention is a combination of brains and material. The more brains you use, the less materials you need."

Test as many student solutions as you deem practical. Be prepared to make judgment calls on possible solutions. Does lighting the candle, melting some wax, and then using the soft wax to stick the candle to the wall qualify as a solution? How about thumbtacking the matchbox to the wall and then setting the candle on the matchbox? Be prepared to make such decisions.

Take Home

The materials used in this activity are common enough that students could easily and safely challenge their parents, siblings, or friends to solve the Off the Wall problem.

Creative Challenges

Creative Challenges Introduction

In each Creative Challenge, the teacher will present a problem (challenge) for you to solve. The teacher will give you a set of guidelines to follow for each challenge. Working within those guidelines, it will be up to you to meet the challenge and solve the problem. As you design and develop a solution to each problem, practice applying the science process skills demonstrated by the teacher in Dynamo Demos: observing, predicting, experimenting, eliminating, and drawing conclusions. You may not use all these steps in each challenge, but the basic process will remain the same.

In each challenge, you will begin with a specific problem to solve. The basic materials for the project will be provided by your teacher, but in some of the challenges, you will be allowed to add materials of your own. You will first observe the materials given and then predict how you might solve the problem. Once you have predicted some possible outcomes to the problem, you can start testing your ideas. In the challenge activities, you will be responsible for setting up and designing your own experiment within the guidelines given by your teacher. As you construct your design, you will need to analyze the different variables involved and eliminate alternatives until you have a reasonable solution. Finally, you will be asked to test your design. You will draw conclusions about the effectiveness of your design and other students' designs.

Suppose you had to solve the following problem: Do aardvarks eat chocolate pudding? If the teacher gave each student an aardvark and chocolate pudding, you would need to set up an experiment to solve the problem. You would have to observe the aardvark to determine his eating habits. You would have to determine how to feed pudding to the aardvark, how often to feed it to him, in what amounts to feed it, etc. Once you established your guidelines for feeding the aardvark the pudding, you would have to try out your experiment to see how it worked. If you were able to get the aardvark to eat the pudding, you would then need to record the results and compare your results with those of your classmates to draw some conclusions.

Of course, your teacher isn't going to give you an aardvark to feed, but we have included one in each challenge as a reminder to you to apply the basic steps of the scientific process as you attempt to solve each problem. Be observant, be creative, and most of all, have fun!

1 Tunnel Time

Challenge

Can you design a tunnel that will hold the greatest amount of weight possible?

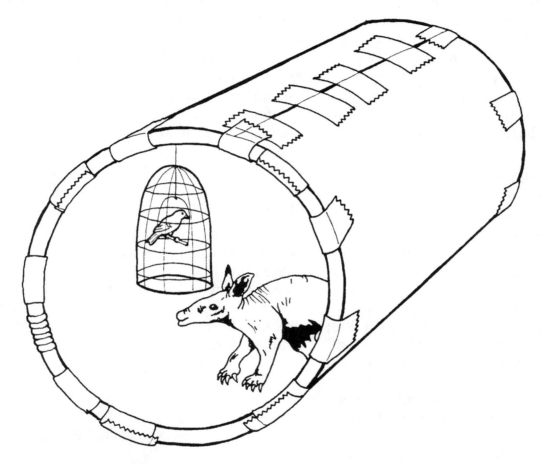

Rules

1. Your teacher will supply you or your design team with the following construction materials:

   • 3 sheets of paper

   • 1 foot of tape (Use it wisely!)

   • 2 plastic drinking straws

2. The completed tunnel can be any shape—triangular, circular, or rectangular—but it must be a minimum of 12 inches long and have a diameter of at least 2 inches at its narrowest point.

3. Your tunnel must be completed within the time limit set by the teacher.

4. Once construction is complete, weights or wet sand will be placed on each tunnel until it collapses. The tunnel holding the most weight will be declared the winning design.

1 For the Teacher

The Challenge

Cave-ins have always been a serious danger in mines. As the depth increases, the pressure on the walls and ceiling of a mine tunnel become enormous. In this activity, students will have to deal with the pressure of designing and constructing a tunnel that will hold the greatest weight possible.

The Rules

1. Have students work in teams.

2. You will need to supply each team with 3 pieces of paper, 12 inches of tape (cellophane or masking), and 2 plastic drinking straws.

3. You will also need a quantity of wet sand (a five-gallon bucket full should be enough); a spoon; scoop or measuring cup; and a large, flat pan (like a cookie sheet).

4. Set a time limit. I suggest you give students one class period to construct their tunnels. Issue the challenge. If working in teams, let students pick their partners the day before. The next day, as students come in, give them their construction supplies and begin. The next day, test the tunnels, record results, clean up, and recognize the winning team.

5. Set minimum dimensions for the tunnels, with minimum diameter being the most important. Otherwise, students will just roll their paper into a tight tube that will never collapse (or that will hold an unrealistic amount of weight). I suggest a minimum length of 12 inches and a minimum diameter of 2 inches. Adjust these numbers as you see fit. The greater the minimum diameter, the greater the challenge.

6. You cannot just scoop wet sand onto the tunnels until they collapse. The sand will roll off and pile up along the sides of the tunnel, preventing them from ever collapsing (the culvert effect). Nor can you stack weights directly on the tunnels without some of the weights falling off. You need to place something flat on top of each tunnel and then pile the weights or sand on this. I take a rectangular piece of thin wood paneling and drill four holes in each corner, making the holes large enough to fit over the rods of a ring stand. I then set up four ring stands on a table, place the tunnel to be tested in the center of the ring stands, and slide the wood piece down over the rods of the ring stands until it rests on the tunnel. I add weights or wet sand until the tunnel collapses. If you use wet sand, set a plastic container on the flat piece resting on the tunnel and scoop the sand into the container. When the tunnel collapses, all you need to do is weigh the container and sand to see how much weight was needed to collapse the tunnel.

Safety Tip

Use common sense.

Awards and Recognition

1. Display a chart explaining the activity and showing the amount of sand held by each team's tunnel.

2. Make and present a "Toughest Tunnel" award to the winning team.

3. Use the cardboard tube in a roll of toilet paper or paper towels to make a gag trophy and present it to the winning student or team.

Display all charts, awards, or trophies where they may be appreciated by other students, teachers, and parents.

2 | Edible Engineering

Challenge

Design an edible car.

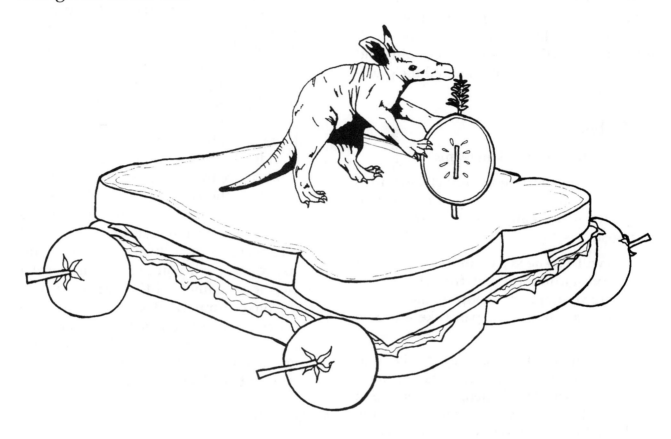

Rules

1. You or your team will supply all the construction materials necessary to build your design.

2. All components of the car must be edible, except the axles. Please use fresh materials as your teacher may let you eat the cars at the conclusion of this activity. Refrigerate all food items before beginning, during construction, and once the car is completed.

3. The car must roll down the full length of a ramp in one piece to qualify as having solved the problem. There is no time limit as to how long it takes the car to roll the distance, but it must reach the bottom of the ramp in a reasonable amount of time.

4. Cars must be completed within the time limit set by the teacher.

In this culinary activity, you have the satisfaction of solving a problem and getting a snack for your efforts.

2 For the Teacher

The Rules

1. Have students work alone or in teams.

2. Students should supply all the materials necessary to construct their design.

3. For these cars to have any chance to actually work, a rigid axle is needed. Thus, the rules allow for toothpicks, wire, and other such construction materials in the axles only.

4. To qualify as a successful solution to the problem, the cars must roll the full length of a ramp in one piece. A car that disintegrates into a pile of vegetables and cookies part way down the ramp does not qualify as having met the challenge successfully.

   Build a simple ramp using a 3- or 4-foot piece of 1×10 or 1×12 lumber (or whatever scraps you can find) elevated on one end by several books. Set reasonable time limits on how long the cars have to make it to the bottom of the ramp. Some cars may never budge from the top of the ramp.

5. Depending on your time restrictions, let students either work on this activity during class time or have them brainstorm, design, and build their cars outside of class. Students should present and explain their cars to the rest of the class during class time.

6. Allow students to eat their designs at the conclusion of the activity.

Safety Tips

This is a fun activity, but food poisoning is no joke. To prevent any possible problems, insist that students follow these safety guidelines:

1. All food items must be as fresh as possible.

2. When not being used in construction, all food items must be refrigerated. Completed cars must be refrigerated at school or home until just before the competition.

3. Wash hands thoroughly before handling food items.

4. Students should not eat anything that has been altered. For example, it would be best not to eat the cookie wheels of a car whose axles were lubricated with spray silicone.

Awards and Recognition

1. If students are thoughtful and build their cars out of something tasty, eating the cars will provide some reward.

2. Award appropriate gag gifts, such as small refrigerator magnets in the form of fruits and vegetables, to all participants.

3 | Cousteau's Contraption

Challenge

Design and build a device that will sink and then resurface as close as possible to a preset time.

Rules

1. You or your team will supply all the construction materials necessary to build your design.

2. The entire device must totally sink. That is, it must go to the bottom of the tank.

3. The entire device or any part of the device must resurface.

4. The device or its parts should resurface as close as possible to the time limit set by the teacher. Points will be awarded according to a system your teacher will explain to you. The device with the highest point total will be declared the winning design.

5. Timing will start when your device strikes the bottom of the tank.

6. Your device should be constructed to fit within the tank. It should be totally underwater when it comes to rest on the bottom of the tank.

7. You may not aid or assist your device in any way once it is placed in the tank.

8. Water will be the liquid used to test your design. No harmful or dangerous liquids will be allowed.

9. Your device must be built within the time limit set by the teacher.

3 For the Teacher

The Challenge

In this activity, students actually have three challenges: one easy, one hard, and one very hard. The easy part is getting their device to sink. The harder part is getting all or any part of their device to resurface. The hardest part is getting the device to resurface precisely at a preset time.

Background Information

This activity is named in memory of Jacques Cousteau, legendary oceanographer, environmentalist, and famed inventor of the scuba system that freed humans to explore watery realms.

The Rules

1. Have students work alone or in teams.

2. Students should supply all the materials necessary to construct their devices.

3. You will need to supply a watertight tank of some kind to sink the devices in. Aquariums, buckets, and even plastic trash cans will work. Whatever you use, it is important that students know the dimensions of the tank well in advance so they can design their devices accordingly.

4. Inform students well in advance of the time limit to resurface. I have found 30 seconds to be a challenging time.

5. Set a time limit on construction of the devices. I have my students work on their devices outside of class for several days to perhaps a week. They bring their devices to school on the day scheduled for testing.

6. Consider having each student or team explain to the rest of the class how their device is supposed to work before they test the device.

7. Test the devices one at a time. Once the device touches the bottom of the tank, begin timing. You can keep time with a stopwatch or have the students count out loud.

8. In this activity, I use zero as a perfect score. For example, if 30 seconds is the resurface time, a device that resurfaced within 20 seconds would earn -10 points, indicating they were under the time limit. A device that resurfaced within one minute would earn a score of + 30, indicating they were over the time limit. Zero would be a perfect score—neither + or –.

Safety Tips

Use only water to test the devices. Caustic or dangerous liquids like acid or bleach should never be allowed.

Awards and Recognition

Display a chart explaining the activity and showing the points earned by each student or team where it can be appreciated by other students, teachers, and parents.

4 | Careful Stacker

Challenge

Is it possible to stack materials in such a way so that the top of the stack lies completely outside the vertical plane of the bottom of the stack?

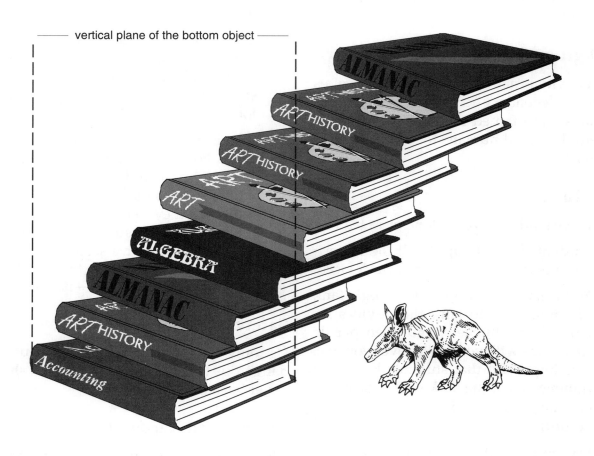

vertical plane of the bottom object

Rules

1. Your teacher will supply you or your design team with objects to stack.

2. Carefully stack your objects so the top of the stack eventually extends beyond the bottom of the stack.

3. The student or team that solves the problem using the most objects will win the "Careful Stacker" award.

4 For the Teacher

The Challenge

Mathematically, there is no limit to how far you can extend the top object over the bottom one if you have an unlimited supply of objects. Strange but true.

The Rules

1. Have students work alone or in teams.

2. You will need to supply objects for the students or teams to stack. Empty pizza boxes, empty video tape boxes, 3 1/2 inch floppy computer disks, and children's wooden blocks will all work for this activity.

3. The student or team that solves the challenge using the most objects should be declared the winner.

Background Information

It is, actually, quite a simple task if you go about it logically. Most students will place the first object on the table. They will then place the second object about half way over the first so that it just balances. They will then try to put a third object over the second at an offset, but they will likely never be able to get their third object to balance!

Here is the trick. Place the objects on top of one another on a table. BEGIN AT THE TOP! Move the top object horizontally until it just begins to teeter. Now go down to the second object We are numbering from the top down. The second object needs to be offset ever so slightly, less than 1/4 of an object length from the object under it. The third object needs to be offset 1/6 of an object length over the object under it. The next objects will have offsets of 1/8, 1/10, 1/12, 1/14 and so on. I suggest you demonstrate this to students at the conclusion of the activity, and I also recommend you practice this before you try it in front of students.

For you mathematicians in the crowd, there is a little relationship you can use to get the exact measurements for the dislocation of each object. The offset of the object is given by $1/2n$, where "n" is the number of the object (numbering from the top) in question. For example, the 3rd object from the top should be offset by $1/(2 \times 3)$, or 1/6, of the length of an object over the object just below it. If you carry this out, it diverges into infinity. So, theoretically, there is no limit to how far you can extend the top object over the bottom one. This seeming paradox may be hard for students to believe. You may want to spend some time discussing why it is theoretically possible to do this, but not actually possible to extend this to unlimited distances.

Safety Tip

Use common sense.

Awards and Recognition

Make a "Careful Stacker" award certificate and present it to the winning student or team. Hang the certificate where it can be appreciated by other students, teachers and parents.

5 Support Your Local Spaghetti

Challenge

Build the tallest support possible, using only spaghetti and tape, that will hold an object for a predetermined time.

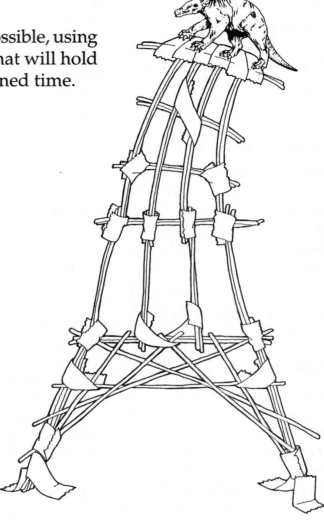

Rules

1. Your teacher will supply you or your design team with the following construction materials:

   - 20 pieces of dry spaghetti

   - 3 feet (36 inches) of masking tape

2. You may use only these materials, but not all the materials have to be used.

3. The pieces of spaghetti may be broken to any length.

4. Your support must be flat on top to hold the object to be supported.

5. Your support should be designed to be (1) as tall as possible and (2) able to support a selected object for a predetermined time.

6. Your device must be completed within the time limit set by the teacher.

7. The winning design will be decided by the following formula:

   height of tower + seconds object is supported = total points

   The teacher will predetermine the maximum time the object must be supported.

5   For the Teacher

The Challenge

Given minimal materials, students are challenged in two ways in this activity: 1) They must not only build a device to support a selected object (weight) for a predetermined time, but 2) they must make the device as tall as possible.

The Rules

1. Have students work alone or in teams.

2. You will need to supply each student or team with 20 pieces of spaghetti and 3 feet (36 inches) of masking tape.

3. The students need to know ahead of time what object (size and weight) must be supported. I suggest using textbooks for your test object. They are heavy enough to present a support challenge, everyone has the same standard object they must support, and you probably have enough of them to go around.

4. The supports must be built in such a way that they can hold the object without it falling off.

5. Students also need to know ahead of time how long their device must support the object. Thirty seconds seems to be a challenging time limit.

6. Use the formula shown on the student page to determine the winning design.

For example, a tower 6.25 inches tall that held an object for 20 seconds would have a point total of 6.25 + 20 or 26.25 points

7. I issue the challenge. Then I set a time limit on construction. I give my students one class period to construct their devices. If students work in teams, I let them pick their partners. The next day, as students come in, they get their building supplies and begin construction. Leave enough time at the end of the period for wrap up and cleanup.

Safety Tip

Use common sense.

Awards and Recognition

1. Display a chart explaining the activity and showing total points scored by each student or team.

2. Make and present the "Stupendous Spaghetti Supporter" award to the winning student or team.

3. Hot glue some pieces of spaghetti together into a gag trophy for the winning student or team.

Display charts, award certificates, or trophies where they may be appreciated by other students, teachers, and parents.

6 Teeny Tiny Towers

Challenge

Given a piece of paper and some tape, construct the tallest free-standing tower possible.

Rules

1. Your teacher will supply you or your design team with the following construction materials:

   • 1 legal-size sheet of paper

   • 3 feet (36 inches) of cellophane tape (Use it wisely!)

2. Your structure cannot be attached to anything other than the floor or table, and it cannot lean against anything.

3. The height of the structure will be measured from the floor to the highest point on the structure.

4. The structure must stand on its own long enough to be measured. You cannot hold up or support your structure while it is being measured.

5. The tallest structure will be declared the winning design.

6. Towers must be constructed within the time limit set by the teacher.

6 For the Teacher

The Challenge

Some tower building activities using newspapers result in structures many feet tall. However, given the few materials allowed in this challenge, these towers will not exactly scrape the sky, hence the name of this challenge.

The Rules

1. Have students work alone or in teams.

2. You will need to supply each student or team with 1 legal-size piece of paper and 3 feet (36 inches) of cellophane tape.

3. The base of the tower must rest on the floor or table. The base may be taped to the floor or table. However, no other part of the structure may be attached to anything, nor may the tower lean against anything for support.

4. The structure must stand without student assistance long enough to be measured. Some towers will stand but droop. How will you measure these? Will you measure from the floor to the highest vertical point on the structure, or will you measure the total length of the tower from base to tip disregarding droop? You need to decide beforehand, and inform students before competition begins.

5. A 6- or 8-foot measuring tape should be more than adequate to determine the height of each structure.

6. Set a time limit. I give my students one class period to construct their towers. I issue the challenge. If students are working in teams, let them pick their partners the day before. The next day, as students come in, they get their supplies and begin construction. Leave enough time at the end of the period for final measurements and cleanup.

Safety Tip

Use common sense.

Awards and Recognition

1. Display a chart explaining the activity and showing the height of each student's or team's tower.

2. Make and present a "Tallest Tower" award to the winning student or team.

3. Glue together some pieces of paper to make a gag trophy and present it to the winning student or team.

Display all charts, awards, or trophies where they may be appreciated by other students, teachers, and parents.

7 | Tacoma Narrows Revisited

Challenge

Design and build a toothpick bridge that will support a maximum load.

Rules

1. The structure of your bridge must be rigid and made of some type of beam.

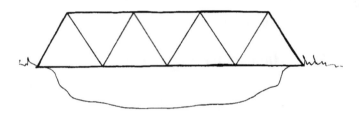

2. The bridge must be no more than 14 inches long and 4 inches high. There is no limit on the width of the bridge. Your bridge will span a 10 inch gap.

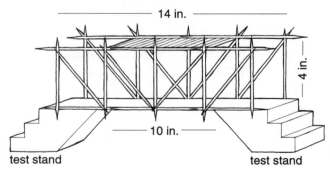

3. The top center span must have a flat area measuring 2 × 2 inches to be used as a loading platform.

4. Only standard flat or round toothpicks may be used. The teacher will supply you or your design team with one box of toothpicks (around 750 toothpicks total). These are all the toothpicks you may use.

5. The toothpicks may be shortened, bent, or spliced.

6. Glue or cement may be applied only at joints (where toothpicks touch) or splices. Toothpicks may not be tied or wired together, and dipping toothpicks in glue to strengthen them is not allowed.

7. There are no restrictions on the type or amount of glue or cement used.

8. Your bridge will be placed on the test stand, a loading block will be placed on the loading platform on your bridge, and weights will be added to the block.

9. Weight will be added until the bridge collapses. The bridge withstanding the greatest load will be declared the winning design.

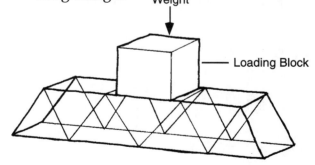

10. Bridges must be completed within the time limit set by the teacher.

7 For the Teacher

The Challenge

This bridge-building activity will give your students a taste of the challenges faced by engineers on a daily basis.

Background Information

This activity is named after one of the most dramatic bridge failures in history. In 1940, the 2,800-foot (853-meter) Tacoma Narrows suspension bridge across the Tacoma Narrows in Washington was completed. Even before it was opened to traffic, there were large up and down movements (vertical oscillations) in the structure. Minor efforts were made to correct the problem, but the bridge still vibrated vertically as much as 4 feet (1.2 meters) on occasion , causing the bridge to be named "Galloping Gertie." On November 7, 1940, while exposed to a wind of 42 miles per hour, the bridge deck suddenly changed from oscillating vertically to twisting horizontally. Under this severe twisting action, the roadway ripped loose and plunged into the water below. The only loss of life was a pet dog left behind in a car as motorists on the bridge fled. The wind won't collapse your students' bridges but they, like Tacoma Narrows, will fail.

The Rules

1. Have students work alone or in teams.

2. Depending on your time restrictions, let students either work on this activity during class time or have them brainstorm, design, and build their bridges outside of class. If bridges are constructed outside the classroom, you will need to supply each student or team with only one box of unopened toothpicks. If bridges are constructed in the classroom, you will need to supply each student or team with toothpicks and various types of glue or cement.

3. Before test day, you will need to secure a set of standardized weights. You might use science weight sets and/or plates borrowed from the athletic weight room of your school. Whatever you use, you need a weight of a known mass.

4. On test day, position two tables 10 inches apart to serve as the test stand. Position each bridge across the gap and add weights until the bridge collapses. The bridge holding the most weight before collapsing should be declared the winning design.

Safety Tips

There is little element of danger in this activity, but (1) be aware that some types of glue or cement can bond human skin and (2) keep students at a safe distance when adding weights to the bridges. You don't want a weight to fall on someone's foot or for flying pieces of toothpick to hit a student in the face.

Awards and Recognition

1. Display a chart explaining the activity and showing the weight each student's or team's bridge held before collapse.

2. Make and present a "Tacoma Narrows" award to the winning student or team.

3. Glue together some toothpicks to make a gag trophy, and present it to the winning student or team.

Display all charts, awards, or trophies where they may be appreciated by other students, teachers, and parents.

8 Mousetrap Madness

Challenge

Design and build a self-contained vehicle that will stop the closest to a measured distance, using a mousetrap as the only source of energy.

Rules

1. The teacher will supply you or your design team with one mousetrap. You must provide everything else you need.

2. The mousetrap may be altered in any way you wish. The vehicle wheel and body size are unrestricted, but it must have at least three wheels.

3. The spring of the mousetrap must be the only energy source used to move your contraption. Your vehicle must be started from a standstill position without the aid of supports. No push or pull starts are allowed.

4. Your vehicle must be built within the time limit set by the teacher.

5. If time permits, you will be given several trial runs. The best performance will be used as the official test run.

6. You will be allowed to adjust or repair your vehicle between trial runs.

7. The vehicle that comes the closest to traveling a measured distance will be declared the winning design. The teacher will inform you of the distance to be traveled before construction begins.

8 For the Teacher

The Challenge

There are many variations of mousetrap car activities, but this one is more challenging than most because rather than going for speed or longest distance, the trick here is to stop after having gone a predetermined distance.

The Rules

1. Have students work alone or in teams.

2. You will need to supply each student or team with one mousetrap. Common mousetraps can be purchased at hardware or grocery stores.

3. Have students work on their designs either during class or outside of class. I present this challenge to my students, hand them their mousetraps, and give them several days to build their devices on their own. The devices are brought to school for the day of the competition. One class period is usually sufficient to give each student or team several trial runs. Before construction begins, inform students of the distance they are trying to get their car to travel. I find 10 feet to be a challenging distance.

4. These cars tend to go all over the place. I suggest holding the competition in a large open area, like a gymnasium.

5. On the day of the competition, place a one-to two-foot piece of masking tape on the floor in an appropriate spot and use a marker to draw a dark line the length of the tape. This will be the official starting line. Now go 10 feet (or whatever distance you've predetermined), and put another piece of tape with a line on it. This is the official stop line.

6. At the start of each run, students must align their cars so that the front end is on the starting line. On your command, have students release their cars and stand back. No one may push, pull, or otherwise aid their car in any way.

7. Once each car comes to a stop, measure the distance from the front of the car to the official stop line. Beforehand, prepare a point system and share it with students. For example, if the front of the car travels exactly 10 feet (or whatever distance you predetermine), award 100 points—a perfect score. For each inch the car stops short or long of the official stop line, deduct one point from a perfect score of 100. Therefore, a car that stops 12 inches over the finishing line would earn a score of 88 while one that stops 3 inches short would score a 97. The car with the score closest to a perfect score should be declared the winning design.

8. Give students or teams as many trial runs as time permits. Count only the best run for each car.

9. Allow students a reasonable amount of time between trial runs to adjust or repair their vehicles as needed.

Safety Tip

Caution students to keep their fingers away from set mousetraps.

Awards and Recognition

1. Display a chart explaining the activity and showing the points earned by each student or team's car.

2. Make and present a "Mousetrap Madness" award to the winner(s).

3. Buy a cheap plastic child's toy car as a gag trophy and present it to the winner(s).

Display all charts, awards, or trophies where they may be appreciated by others.

9 Captain Capsize

Challenge

Design and build a clay boat that will hold as much weight as possible before sinking.

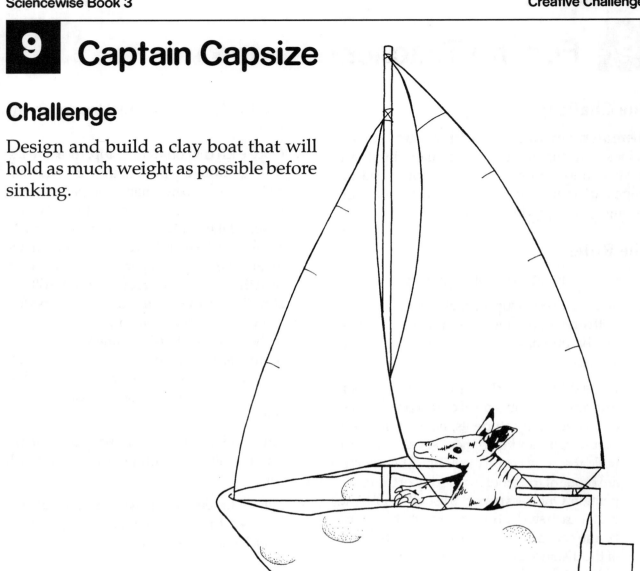

Rules

1. The teacher will provide you or your design team with a set amount of modeling clay. You are not allowed to use any other materials.

2. There are no restrictions for the boat size, weight, or design. However, no devices (rolling pins, etc.) may be used to form or shape the boat.

3. The boat must be constructed to fit within the test tank.

4. The boat must be completed within the time limit set by the teacher.

5. Once your boat is completed, it will be floated in a container of water. You will add uniform weights to the boat one at a time until the boat sinks, while a second team member or another person keeps the boat from touching the sides of the container with a soda straw.

6. The winning design will be the boat that holds the most weight before it sinks.

9 For the Teacher

The Challenge

There are a number of variations of boat-building activities, but this one is more challenging than most because of the minimal construction materials students are allowed to use.

The Rules

1. Have students work alone or in teams.

2. You will need to supply each student or team with a measured amount of non-water soluble modeling clay. I have found 4 to 5 ounces (around 125 grams) to be a challenging amount.

3. You will also need to set up a tank of water ahead of time. A 5-gallon aquarium should suffice, but a 10-gallon aquarium would be even better as it could accommodate extra-large boats.

4. I suggest using pennies for weights to test the boats. They are uniform size and weight and easy to handle and count. You can either express the total pennies held by each boat or convert the number of pennies to a total weight held. One penny weighs approximately 0.1 ounce (2.5 grams).

5. The day before, I weigh a ball of clay for each team and set up the test tank. The next day, as the students (or teams) come in, they get their clay. I issue the challenge and let the students pick teams (if you wish them to work in teams). Set a time limit for construction. I give my students one class period to construct their boats. Leave enough time at the end of the period for final testing and cleanup.

6. When students or teams have completed their boats, have them bring the boats to the test tank. Have the student or one of the team members place the pennies on the boat while another team member or student carefully uses a soda straw to keep the boat from touching the sides of the test tank. For effect and accuracy, I have the entire class count as each penny is added.

7. Things can get a little wet during this activity, so have some towels handy.

8. The boat that holds the most pennies before it totally sinks should be declared the winning design. Occasionally, boats will have water come over the top but not totally sink until a few more pennies are added. I suggest you keep adding pennies and counting until each boat totally sinks. Students should be made aware in advance how you will handle this situation should it arise.

Safety Tip

You might caution students about putting pennies in their mouths.

Awards and Recognition

1. Display a chart explaining the activity and showing the number of pennies each student's or team's boat floated.

2. Make and present a "Captain Capsize" award to the winning student or team.

3. Buy a cheap plastic child's toy boat as a gag trophy, and present it to the winning student or team.

Display all charts, awards, or trophies where they may be appreciated by other students, teachers, and parents.

10 The Wright Stuff

Challenge

Make a single sheet of paper land as close as possible to the center of a target.

Rules

1. You will be given two sheets of paper, both the same size.

2. Your "airplane" must be made from only one sheet of paper or the pieces cut from one piece of paper. Use one sheet of paper for practice and the other for the actual competition.

3. The sheet of paper may be folded or cut in any way you choose.

4. Tape, staples, and/or paper clips may be used to hold pieces of your "airplane" together. Nothing else may be attached to your plane. Remember—the heavier the design, the faster it will fall.

5. You may not wad up the paper and throw it.

6. Only one "airplane" per person or group may be entered.

7. Each plane will be hand launched but cannot be touched or aided in any way after launch.

8. Each person or group will be allowed as many trial runs as time permits. Only the run closest to the target will be counted.

9. The plane that lands the closest to the target (scores the most points) will be declared the winning design.

10. Your plane must be built within the time limit set by the teacher.

10   For the Teacher

The Challenge

There are a number of paper airplane activities, but this one is particularly challenging because it is based on accuracy.

Background Information

This activity is named in honor of the Wright brothers, Wilbur and Orville, who designed, built, and flew the world's first mechanically powered aircraft off the sands of Kitty Hawk, North Carolina. Hopefully, your students will show some of the same ingenuity and creativity that the Wright brothers did.

The Rules

1. Have students work alone or in teams.

2. Provide each student or team with two sheets of paper, both the same size. The size of paper is up to you. (Standard 8.5 " x 11" paper works well.)

3. You will also need to provide tape, a stapler, and paper clips in case students or teams wish to incorporate them into their designs.

4. Require student designs to at least somewhat resemble an airplane. Don't allow students to wad up the paper and throw it.

5. Set a time limit. I allow my students to work on their designs at school during class time. I set aside several periods for design, construction, and testing and one period for the competition.

6. Hold the competition indoors in a large area like a gymnasium or outside in a parking lot if there is no wind.

7. Each student or someone from each team must hand launch the plane-assisted take-offs. Using rubber bands, etc., is not allowed.

8. Use masking tape to mark a starting line on the floor. Launch all planes from this line.

9. Give each student or team as many trial runs as time permits, but count only the run closest to the target.

10. A measuring tape will be needed to determine distance to target for each plane. A 10- or 12-foot tape should be sufficient if you use the scoring system shown below.

11. Place a target a reasonable distance away. What you use for a target is up to you. You can determine a reasonable and challenging distance for the target by carefully observing earlier test flights.

12. Use a system of scoring similar to this:
    hitting target = 10 points
    within 6 inches = 9 points
    12 inches = 8 points
    18 inches = 7 points
    24 inches = 6 points
    30 inches = 5 points
    within 36 inches = 4 points
    beyond 36 inches = 1 point

Safety Tip

Use common sense.

Stumped?

If available, books on making paper airplanes might serve as a guide and inspiration.

Awards and Recognition

1. Display a chart explaining the activity and showing the points each student's or team's plane scored. You might also display each student's or team's plane as well.

2. Make and present a "Wright Stuff" award to the winning student or team.

3. Buy a small plastic toy airplane as a gag trophy and present it to the winning student or team.

11 Catch Some Rays

Challenge

Design and construct a device that will use solar power (heat) to melt an ice cube as fast as possible.

Rules

1. The teacher will supply one or more premeasured ice cubes. You or your team must provide everything else.

2. The device must be designed so that only solar power (heat) melts the ice cube. No other form of heating—electricity, burning paper, etc., will be allowed.

3. You may not use magnifying glasses or glass or plastic lenses as part of your device. However, you may use anything else you want in the construction of your device.

4. The maximum size of the finished device can be no more than 2 cubic feet.

5. The device must be constructed so that the ice cube can be seen or so that the ice cube can be easily accessed for observation purposes.

6. Once your device has been loaded with an ice cube and set in the sun, you will be allowed to change the orientation of your device but no other adjustments will be permitted.

7. The device that completely melts the ice cube in the shortest amount of time will be declared the winning design.

8. Your device must be completed within the time limit set by the teacher.

11 For the Teacher

The Challenge

The solar energy that strikes the earth is tremendous. The total annual energy consumption of the entire United States is only about two-hundredths of a percent of the solar energy falling on this country each year.

People tap solar energy in many different ways, but the most common methods are using solar collectors for heating and photovoltaic cells to convert sunlight into electricity.

This activity will challenge your students to design a solar collector that will harness the energy of the sun as efficiently as possible.

The Rules

1. From a time and materials standpoint, it is best to have students work in teams on this activity.

2. You will need to provide each team with several standard size ice cubes. Allow each team several ice cubes for test purposes, and keep one for the actual competition. Make standard ice cubes by carefully measuring a set amount of water into the compartments of ice cube trays. About 20 milliliters (0.70 ounces) makes a nice size cube. The exact size and shape of the cube doesn't matter (but don't make them too large, or they may take too long to melt) as long as the students know the size and shape of the cubes ahead of time so they can design their devices accordingly.

3. Only the heat generated by the sun should be used to melt the ice cube. Do not allow electric heaters, burning paper, or any other such heating devices to be part of any team's design.

4. Put a size limitation of 2 cubic feet maximum on any design. Shape should not be a problem and really doesn't need to be regulated.

5. The only restrictions on building materials are that teams should not use magnifying glasses, glass, or plastic lenses in their devices. Anything else is fair game.

6. You will need to be able to see or access the ice cube during the competition to observe speed of melting. The device must be constructed so that the ice cube can be easily accessed for observation purposes.

7. Set a reasonable time limit on construction of the devices. I suggest you allow students several days to a week to work on their designs outside of class. Have them bring their devices to school the day before the competition. This will allow you to examine the devices to see that each one complies with the rules and will also allow a one-day grace period to those who forget to bring their devices on the assigned day. The next day, set aside the entire class period for the competition (and hope for sunny weather).

8. On the day of the competition, load each device with a standard ice cube then place each device in the same general sunny location. I have found the school parking lot or a sidewalk in front of the school to be an excellent location to place these devices. The clock should start when all the devices have been placed.

9. As the competition progresses, allow students to move and change their device's orientation in relation to the sun but do not allow any other adjustments.

10. The device that melts the ice cube completely in the shortest amount of time should be declared the winning design.

Safety Tips

A well-designed solar collector can get hot enough inside to cook food. Students should be aware of this and handle their devices accordingly.

Stumped?

Instruct students to use materials that reflect sunlight and shapes that focus the sun's rays. It might be helpful to have students research solar collectors before they begin construction.

Awards and Recognition

1. Display a chart explaining the activity and showing the time it took each team's device to melt the ice cube.

2. Display some or all of the students' devices.

3. Make and present a "Magnificent Ray Catcher" award to the winning team.

Display all charts, awards, or trophies where they may be appreciated by parents, students, and teachers.

12 The Don Quixote Device

Challenge

Design and build a wind machine that will pull a weight across a horizontal distance in the shortest possible time.

Rules

1. The device must fit within an imaginary box: 10 inches (24 centimeters) × 4 in. (10 cm) × 8 in. (20 cm).

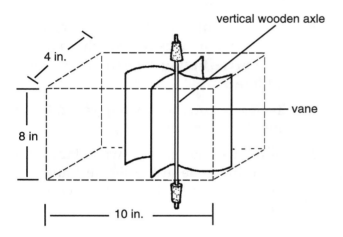

2. The device must be mounted on a stand so that the axle will be in a position to wind up a string to which a weight has been attached.

3. The only restriction on what materials may be used in constructing your device is that the vertical wooden axle should

be made of a 3/16 inch dowel no longer than 12 inches (30 centimeters).

4. Collapsible vanes or vanes with moving parts may be used.

5. On the day of the competition, your wind device will be placed on the floor in front of a fan. The distance from the fan to each device will be the same.

6. 13 feet (4 meters) of string will be attached to the axle or take-up spool of your device.

7. The time it takes the weight to pass across the timing zone after the initial "start-up" zone will be recorded. Each device will get several trial runs as time allows, but only the best run will be counted.

8. The wind device that pulls (winds) the weight the fastest through the timing zone will be declared the winning design.

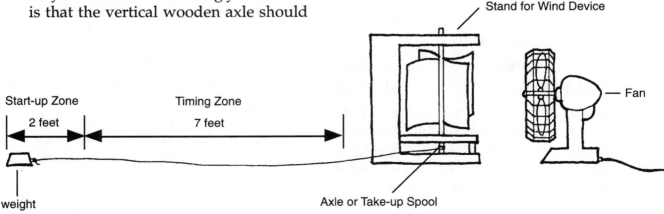

12 For the Teacher

The Challenge

The phrase "tilting at windmills," meaning to fight against an imaginary difficulty, has become part of our language through "Don Quixote." This activity will have your students jousting a challenge that may leave them as frustrated as Don Quixote.

Background Information

Don Quixote was Cervantes's fictional Spanish character who believed the exaggerated romances of chivalry of his day to be true. Declaring himself a knight-errant, he set forth on his old horse. Don Quixote regarded everything he saw as extraordinary. Inns were castles and windmills were giants that he attempted to subdue in battle.

The Rules

1. Have students work alone or in teams.

2. There is a size restriction (see the student section) for the device but no restriction on the materials that may be used to construct the device. You might consider supplying the wooden dowel to be used as a vertical axle. Dowel rods may be purchased for a reasonable price from lumber yards or hardware stores.

3. A large box fan should supply enough air to power the devices. Use caution as to the power setting on your fan. Some of your students' devices may be somewhat fragile, and a high wind speed could tear them apart.

4. On the day of the competition, use masking tape to mark off 5 lines on the floor.

5. Lines 1 and 2 mark the distance each device should be from the fan. The exact distance between lines 1 and 2 is up to you. I suggest doing a few trial runs and then deciding the best spacing between devices and fan.

6. Lines 3 and 4 should be 7 feet apart and represent the timing zone.

7. Lines 4 and 5 should be 2 feet apart and represent the "start-up" zone.

8. To test each device, attach 13 feet (4 meters) of string to the axle of the device. Attach a weight to the other end of the string. What you use for the weight and how heavy a weight you use is up to you. I have found that a silver dollar works nicely. See the illustration on the following page.

9. The fan should now be turned on. Time the interval it takes the weight to travel through the timing zone (between line 4 and line 3).

10. Give each student or group several trial runs as time permits.

11. The device that pulls the weight through the timing zone in the shortest amount of time should be declared the winning design.

Safety Tip

Use common sense.

Stumped?

Prior to designing and building their devices, students might wish to undertake a study of windmills: American multiblade, Dutch four-arm, High-speed propeller, Savonius, Flettner, or Stuart propeller-type.

Awards and Recognition

1. Display a chart explaining the activity and showing the time it took each student's or team's device to wind up the weight. You might also display each student's or team's device as well.

2. Make and present a "Wonderful Wind-mill" award to the winning student or team.

Display all charts, awards, or trophies where they may be appreciated by other students, teachers, and parents.

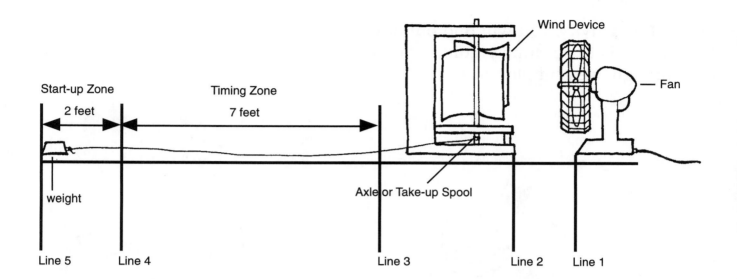

13 Program Your "Robot"

Challenge

In this activity, you will find out how hard it is to accurately guide a robot through even simple tasks.

Rules

1. You will work as a team with another student.

2. One team member will be the controller and the other team member will be the robot.

3. The person playing the robot will be securely blindfolded.

4. The robot, following verbal instructions from the controller, must move along a prescribed obstacle course, and then deposit a ball in a container.

5. The robot cannot talk and must follow the directions given to it exactly ("turn right" doesn't mean all parts of the body or 90° right.)

6. After the robot has successfully put the ball in the container, the robot and the controller should switch again.

7. The team with the lowest average time (both robots' times averaged) will be declared the winning controllers.

13   For the Teacher

The Challenge

Until robots become true "thinking" machines, able to understand their environment and make decisions about what to do to accomplish their mission, they will depend on controllers to guide them. In this activity, students will find out how hard it is to accurately control and guide a "robot" (their partner) through even a simple task.

The Rules

1. Ahead of time, construct an obstacle course/maze in your classroom. This activity is harder than it first appears, so do not make the obstacle course/maze too difficult or the teams may not be able to complete the assigned task.

2. The only materials required are a tennis ball or baseball; a container, like a trash can, to put the ball in; a blindfold; and a stopwatch.

3. Have students work in teams of two. Designate one student as the controller and the other student as the "robot."

4. The controller should guide the blindfolded robot through the obstacle course/maze using only verbal command. The robot cannot speak and must follow all commands exactly as given by the controller. Time how long it takes the robot to complete the task.

5. Once the robot completes the task, team members should switch roles and try again. Again, time how long it takes the robot to complete the task.

6. Average the two times. The team with the lowest average time to complete the task should be declared the winning controllers.

Safety Tip

Use common sense.

Extension

1. Set up a different obstacle course/maze, and try it again. This time, have each team draw a map of the route the robot is supposed to take. The controller will sit facing away from the course the robot must follow. The controller must use the map to keep track of the robot's location and is allowed to ask the robot only "yes" and "no" questions as to its location and surroundings. The robot must await the controller's instructions before moving.

2. The minimum round-trip time for a signal between Earth and Mars is 8.8 minutes; the maximum time is 41.9 minutes. Have students consider how they would change their commands if they took 20 or 30 minutes to reach their robot.

Awards and Recognition

1. Display a chart explaining the activity and showing the time required for each robot to complete the assigned task.

2. Make and present a "Champion Controllers" award to the winning team.

Display all charts, contraptions, and awards where they may be appreciated by other students, teachers, and parents.

14 Brain Games

Challenge

In science and engineering, groups of people often get together to offer possible solutions or alternatives to problems. These meetings are called "brainstorming" sessions. Your team will be asked to "brainstorm" creative solutions to the problems presented below.

Rules

1. You will work as a team with at least one other student.

2. Write down responses to the problems given below with as many answers as possible.

3. There are no "right" or "wrong" answers. However, the answer should be relevant to the problem.

4. Each team will earn points based on the number of answers they generate (1 answer = 1 point).

5. The team with the highest point total will be declared the Brain Game champions.

Problems

1. How many ways can you think of to produce electricity?

2. How many ways can you think of to move a vehicle without an engine?

3. How many things can you think of to do with soil (dirt)?

4. How many new emotions can you invent?

5. How many things can you list that are impossible?

6. How many reasons can you list for doing away with computers?

7. How many ways can you think of to prevent spilling hot coffee while driving?

8. How many uses can you think of for a wooden coat hanger?

9. How many things can you think of to do with cellophane tape?

10. How many ways can you think of to prevent a candle from burning down?

11. How many ways can you think of to pick up a potato off the floor without bending over?

12. How many uses can you think of for a wooden pencil?

14 For the Teacher

The Challenge

This activity consists of brainteasers designed to "stretch the imagination" and stimulate creative problem solving.

The Rules

1. Have students work in teams of two, if possible, or three if necessary. Larger teams are often unwieldy and may present problems.

2. Use the problems given in the student section as you see fit. Feel free to add your own problems or delete or modify the ones given.

3. Assign a point total to each team's answers. Be prepared to reject some answers. Competitive zeal will result in some ridiculous, inappropriate, or irrelevant answers.

4. The team with the highest point total should be declared the Brain Game champions.

Safety Tip

Use common sense.

Awards and Recognition

1. Display a chart explaining the activity and showing the point total of each team.

2. Make and present a "Brain Game Champion" award to the winning team.

Display all charts, awards, or trophies where they may be appreciated by other students, teachers, and parents.

15 The Always Amazing Magnetic-Levitation Device

Challenge

Design and build an electromagnet that will pick up the most iron nails.

Rules

1. The electromagnet should not be larger than 2 × 2 × 2 inches (5 × 5 × 5 centimeters).

2. One surface of the electromagnet will have a hook or loop for holding or hanging the electromagnet. The side opposite the hook or loop will be the pickup surface.

3. Two electrical leads at least 8 inches (20 centimeters) should be attached to the electromagnet.

4. There are no other limitations on construction materials.

5. Your electromagnet will be connected to a 12-volt direct current power source and judged on the number of nails it will levitate (pick up).

6. The electromagnet that picks up the greatest number of nails will be declared the winning design.

15 For the Teacher

The Challenge

By seeing which team can levitate (pick up) the most nails, this activity and the competition it generates will give your students a practical application of the principles of electromagnetism.

The Rules

1. From a time and materials standpoint, you may find it more convenient to have your students work in teams of two or three on this activity.

2. You will need a 12-volt direct current power source to power the electromagnets. A car battery will work, but it is heavy and somewhat difficult to move around.

3. Students should know before construction begins what exact power source will be used. This will allow them to design their electrical leads accordingly so that they may be attached to the power source.

4. You will need to supply the nails used in the competition. Nails may be purchased through lumber yards or hardware stores or perhaps you can borrow some nails from your industrial technology department. I suggest you use small nails in this activity. Some of the electromagnets may not be strong enough to pick up even one large nail. The more nails the electromagnets can pick up, the more lively the competition.

5. You can judge the effectiveness of each electromagnet by merely counting the number of nails each electromagnet lifts or, more accurately, by determining the weight of nails each electromagnet can lift.

6. The electromagnet that picks up the greatest number or weight of nails should be declared the winning design.

Safety Tips

If you use a car battery as a power source, remember that car batteries have powerful acid inside and should be handled carefully.

Stumped?

You might have your students research what electromagnets are and how they work before they begin the design phase of this activity.

Awards and Recognition

1. Display a chart explaining the activity and showing the number of nails or the weight of nails lifted by each electromagnet.

2. Make and present a "Magnificent Magnetic Levitator" award to the winning team.

3. Present the winning team with some magnetic trinket, like a refrigerator magnet, as a gag trophy.

Display all charts, awards, or trophies where they may be appreciated by other students, teachers, and parents.

16 Newton's Wild Ride

Challenge

Design and build the wildest roller coaster ride you can that delivers a marble safely to the end.

Rules

1. You will work in teams on this activity.

2. Each team will get the following construction supplies:

   - 1 or more lengths of pipe insulation
   - tape
   - marble
   - scissors

3. Use the scissors to cut the pipe insulation in half lengthwise to make two long chutes.

4. Using classroom furniture and materials (use books as supports and the pipe insulation as "track"), build a roller coaster.

5. Use tape to hold the coaster in place.

6. Make the turns and dips as tight as possible and don't forget loops.

7. Your goal is to build the wildest ride you can that still delivers the marble safely to the end.

8. Your coaster must be completed within the time limit set by the teacher.

9. Each coaster will be given several trial runs as time permits, and each coaster will be judged on the following formula:

   Average speed (length of "track" divided by time) + Safety (+5 points if the marble stays on the track to the end but –5 points if the marble flies off the track) + Number of turns, hills, and loops + Originality (up to a maximum of 10 points).

10. The coaster with the highest point total will be declared the winning design.

16 For the Teacher

The Challenge

Isaac Newton never had a chance to ride a roller coaster. The first one was built 75 years after his death. But the principles involved in roller coaster design are right down Sir Isaac's alley. In this activity, your students will struggle with the same Newtonian principles that actual coaster designers must contend with on every turn and loop.

Background Information

Newton's laws of motion describe how forces determine the motion of objects. Designers rely on the acceleration caused by those forces to make a roller coaster ride both thrilling and safe. The trick is knowing how to use the forces properly. If the forces are too great in one direction, for instance, they'll throw the car off the track. If an upward force is too large (giving you a feeling of heaviness), your heart cannot pump enough blood to your head and you faint. On the other hand, the lack of supporting forces can create feelings of incredible lightness. This can provide an electrifying ride that delivers you safely to the end.

To keep forces at safe levels, the designer has to stretch out the time and the distance it takes to make changes in direction and speed. This spreads the change over time, decreasing the force you feel. The top of the next hill has to be high enough to slow the coaster down, or stretched out to a gentler or banked curve, so the car doesn't fly off the track.

Space is also a problem. Coasters go forward two feet for every foot they climb. If the highest hill is 100 feet, it takes about 200 horizontal feet to get the car that high. If the highest hill is 200 feet, it takes 400 feet. Since land is expensive, the designers have to be creative about the use of space. A track shaped into a curve takes up less space than one in a straight line.

The Rules

1. From a time and materials standpoint, I suggest you have your students work in teams of two or three on this activity.

2. You will need to provide the following construction supplies to each team:

- 1 or more lengths of pipe insulation. Pipe insulation may be purchased from hardware stores or most retailers that sell plumbing supplies. The students will cut the insulation in half so one piece of insulation will make a "track" twice as long as the original piece of insulation. For example, a 10-foot piece of insulation will make 20 feet of "track."

- Tape to hook the pieces of track together and to attach the track to supporting structures.

- 1 marble per group. Each team's marble should be the same size, and the marbles should fit in the groove made by cutting the pipe insulation in half.

- Scissors to cut the pipe insulation.

3. Use classroom furniture and other materials, such as books, as supports for the coasters. Students will need to tape their coasters to these supports.

4. It really won't work to have students build their coasters at home and then bring them to school on the day of the competition so plan on making room and time for them to do this activity in the classroom.

5. Use the scoring formula shown under 9 on the student section to evaluate each coaster. I suggest allowing each coaster as many trial runs as time permits and then counting the highest point run for each coaster.

---

6. The coaster with the highest point total should be declared the winning design.

Safety Tip

Use care when cutting pipe with scissors.

Stumped?

You might find it helpful to have your students review Newton's laws before they begin this activity.

Awards and Recognition

1. Display a chart explaining the activity and showing the point total earned by each team's coaster.

2. Make and present a "Champion Coaster Creator" award to the winning team.

Display all charts, awards, or trophies where they may be appreciated by other students, teachers, and parents.

Extension

If you and your students would like to carry this activity further, consider building a hypercoaster. A hypercoaster is one that is about twice as tall as a regular roller coaster. Make your hills higher, and experiment with how tight you can make your turns and loops. Have fun but remember, in the end, Sir Isaac's laws will rule.

17 | Mr. Goldberg Turns the Crank

Challenge

One big challenge engineers face when designing a machine is how to transfer one kind of motion to another. For instance, on an airplane, the pistons in the engine move back and forth, but they drive the propeller around in a circular motion.

The challenge in this activity is to design and build a machine that will turn the crank on a manual pencil sharpener.

Background Information

Rube Goldberg was a cartoonist who invented fantastic machines (on paper) to do simple tasks. For instance, to make a piece of toast, he might suggest that if you stepped on a cat's tail, the cat would jump up, knocking over a wastebasket, which would release a ball that would roll down a ramp, pushing down the lever on your toaster. The device you will design and construct to turn the crank of a pencil sharpener will be what is called a "Rube Goldberg contraption."

Rules

1. You will work in teams on this activity.

2. There are no limitations on the materials you can use for construction supplies—if you think it will work, you can use it. The teacher will supply the pencil sharpener.

3. The only restriction is that your machine, not your hands, turn the crank of the pencil sharpener.

17   For the Teacher

The Challenge

This is a challenge that Rube Goldberg would have loved. Invent a machine, or a series of machines, to perform one simple function. The simple function will be to turn the crank on a manual pencil sharpener.

The Rules

1. From a time and materials standpoint, I suggest you have your students work in teams of two or three on this activity.

2. You will need to supply manual pencil sharpeners. Two or three sharpeners should be enough. Your custodial staff may have several nonfunctioning ones in a janitorial closet or perhaps you could borrow several new ones from central supply. I suggest you attach each sharpener to a piece of wood. This will make the sharpener more stable and allow you to add weight if necessary to keep the sharpener from falling over during testing of the students' devices.

Safety Tip

Use common sense.

Awards and Recognition

1. You might display some or all of the devices where they can be seen and appreciated by students, staff, and parents.

2. You might present small hand-held pencil sharpeners as gag trophies to the members of each team that successfully meet the challenge.

Extension

Want to really complicate your students' lives? Challenge them to design a device that will not only turn the crank of a manual pencil sharpener but also actually sharpen a pencil at the same time. This would involve figuring out a way to keep the pencil in place while it is being sharpened.

18 The Itsy Bitsy Spider Climbed Up the Water Spout

Challenge

Design and build a climbing device that will climb vertically through a 4-inch (10-centimeter) inside diameter plastic pipe 3.5 feet (1 meter) tall as quickly as possible.

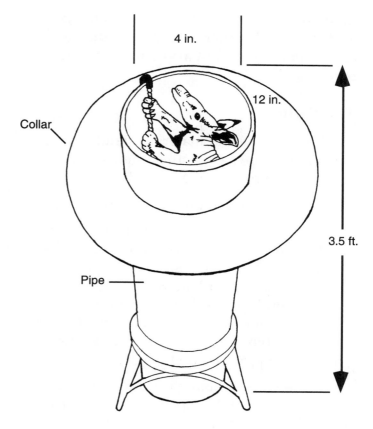

Collar

4 in.

12 in.

3.5 ft.

Pipe

Rules

1. You will work in teams on this activity.

2. The teacher will supply the plastic pipe and stand. Your team must supply all other materials necessary to construct your device.

3. The materials used to construct your device and the source of power you choose to use must be safe. For example, using a model rocket engine to shoot your device up the pipe will not be allowed.

4. Your device may be no longer than 9 inches (24 centimeters) long.

5. The plastic pipe will be placed in a vertical position, and a collar will be placed around the pipe approximately 12 inches (30 centimeters) below the top of the pipe.

6. You will load your device into the bottom of the pipe. The teacher will provide something to hold it there until activated. Timing will begin as soon as your device starts climbing. Timing will stop when your device falls to the collar after emerging from the top of the pipe. In other words, your entire device must exit the pipe.

7. Each device will be given several trial runs as time permits.

8. The device that crawls up and out of the pipe in the shortest time will be declared the winning design.

18 For the Teacher

The Challenge

In this activity, your students are challenged to design and construct a device that will crawl not only up, but also out of a vertical pipe.

The Rules

1. From a time and materials standpoint, I suggest you have your students work in teams of two or three on this activity.

2. You will need to provide the following:

- 1 piece of plastic pipe 3.5 feet (1 meter) long and 4 inches (10 centimeters) in diameter (You may purchase a piece of plastic pipe at a hardware store or any retail outlet that sells plumbing supplies. If you know a plumber and practice a little diplomacy, perhaps you can get a piece of pipe donated to your school.)

- something to hold each device up into the bottom of the pipe until the device is activated and starts climbing (A wooden spatula will work well for this purpose.)

3. Set the pipe up vertically and attach a collar of foam rubber or cardboard as shown in the student section.

4. Give each device as many trial runs as time permits. Count only the fastest run.

5. The device that crawls up and out of the pipe in the shortest time should be declared the winning design.

Safety Tips

The materials used to construct the device and the source of power students use must be safe. Launching a model rocket up the pipe might technically meet the challenge, but it wouldn't be very safe. I suggest you tell your students before they start designing that if there is any doubt about the safety of their device, they should clear the design with you before they ever start construction.

Awards and Recognition

1. Display a chart explaining the activity and showing the time it took each device to climb up and out the pipe.

2. Display the pipe and each team's devices.

3. Make and present an "Itsy Bitsy Spider" award to the winning team.

Display all charts, awards, or trophies where they may be appreciated by other students, teachers, and parents.